Josey sensed that people were covertly watching her.

She could feel the curiosity of their eyes resting on her. So this was the woman who was living with Tom Quinn. However, she could hardly stand here and announce to the assembled company, 'It's not what you think.'

And Tom wasn't exactly helping matters, standing so close behind her like that, as possessive as a dog with a bone. No one looking at them would doubt that they were lovers . . .

Dear Reader

In this year of European unity, July sees the launch in hardback (September paperback) of an intriguing new series—contemporary romances by your favourite Mills & Boon authors, but with a distinctly European flavour. Look out for the special cover of a love story every month set in one of the twelve EC countries, which will take you on a fascinating journey to see the sights, life and romance, Continental style.

Vive l'amour in 1992—who do *you* think is Europe's sexiest hero?

The Editor

Susanne McCarthy grew up in South London but she always wanted to live in the country, and shortly after her marriage she moved to Shropshire with her husband. They live in a house on a hill with lots of dogs and cats. She loves to travel—but she loves to come home. As well as her writing, she still enjoys her career as a teacher in adult education, though she only works part-time now.

Recent titles by the same author:

DANCE FOR A STRANGER
A CANDLE FOR THE DEVIL

SECOND CHANCE FOR LOVE

BY

SUSANNE McCARTHY

by Mills & Boon Limited

© Susanne McCarthy 1990

MILLS & BOON LIMITED
ETON HOUSE   18-24 PARADISE ROAD
RICHMOND   SURREY   TW9 1SR

First published in Great Britain 1992
by Mills & Boon Limited

© Susanne McCarthy 1992

Australian copyright 1992
Philippine copyright 1992
This edition 1992

ISBN 0 263 77645 X

Set in Times Roman 10½ on 12 pt.
01-9208-51200 C

Made and printed in Great Britain

CHAPTER ONE

'Maniac!' The driver of the delivery-van almost had to stand on his brakes, swerving sharply to avoid a head-on collision as the white Porsche took the bend too wide, veering over towards the oncoming traffic. 'Look where you're damned well going,' he advised fiercely, though the woman at the wheel would not have heard him.

In fact, Josey had barely even been aware of the near-accident. She had driven all the way from London in a kind of trance. All she had in the car were the few clothes she had thrown into a bag. Everything else she had left behind her, along with nine years of her life.

She had known for a long time that her marriage was over. But it had come as a bitter blow when Colin had announced, as coolly as you liked, that he wanted a divorce—so that he could marry his secretary. It wasn't losing him that hurt. No, it was the fact that Paula was pregnant—and that he was delighted.

He had never wanted *her* to have children, she reminded herself, the bitterness welling up. A baby wouldn't fit in with their lifestyle, he had said. He worked hard all day, he had said. He didn't want to come home to a house full of toys and nappies, and be kept awake all night by a baby crying.

Maybe she should have left him years ago. But somehow there had never seemed to be quite enough reason to take such a serious step—vague suspicions that he was having affairs, which she had never quite been able to bring herself to confront him with. She was sure Paula wasn't the first—he probably seduced all his secretaries. She ought to know—she had been his secretary herself once.

She had been just twenty-one when she had first gone to work for him—and he had been the stuff of every young girl's dreams: good-looking, urbane and dynamic. Too dynamic for the respectable, well-established firm he was in—he was keen to branch out on his own. He had exercised all his considerable charm to persuade her to take the plunge, and go with him.

It had been fun, at first, watching the small company mushroom with success. But she had always kept their relationship strictly business—she had already had a very nice boyfriend, to whom she was unofficially engaged. Ironically, it was a row with Derek about the long hours she was working that had precipitated the change. Colin had been so incredibly kind and understanding. He had taken her out to dinner to cheer her up—and somehow she had found herself in his bed.

Why, out of all his conquests, had he chosen to marry her? Probably to secure her loyalty, at a time when she would have been indispensable to the business, she mused wryly. And he had probably seen her as a social asset, too—someone to organise the vitally important social side of his life, preside over his dinner parties with grace, making intelligent conversation with all his tedious guests.

And of course she had been beautiful then. She hardly recognised herself now in the thin, pallid creature she had become. Her hair was lank and lifeless, the russet glints it had once held dimmed, and her eyes were dull. She was only thirty-one, but she looked nearer forty. Maybe she couldn't blame him for looking elsewhere.

It was hard to know when it had all started to go wrong. Maybe it was since she had given up her career. She had been overjoyed when Colin had first suggested that, since the company was prospering so well, she no longer needed to work; at last, she had believed, it was his intention that they should start a family. But she had been in for a bitter disappointment.

In the beginning she had tried to persuade him. But every time she had brought the subject up he had accused her of nagging, and eventually he had begun to get more and more annoyed. She had hated the rows, so gradually she had ceased to even try to discuss the issue.

And gradually they had grown further and further apart. She had already grown disillusioned with their shallow lifestyle, with friends who seemed as disposable as last year's fashions. If they could even have had a proper house with a garden to tend, and maybe room for a dog, she might have been a little happier. But their ultra-smart City apartment had begun to seem like a prison: she had been bored, with nothing to do but shop and go the hairdressers—and that hollow, aching longing for a baby had never gone away.

With a hand that shook slightly she reached out to the dashboard, and found the half-empty pack of cigarettes. That was something else, she mused bitterly as she fumbled for her lighter. She had only begun smoking a couple of years ago, to calm her nerves. She had tried countless times to give them up—it was a habit she hated—but she couldn't do without them.

Colin had caught her by surprise, coming home in the middle of the afternoon like that. She had been slopping around the apartment in a pair of old jeans and a faded T-shirt. Somehow that made it all so much worse—he liked a woman to be elegant, and the look of faintly veiled contempt in his eyes had undermined any hope she might have had of dealing with the situation with any kind of dignity.

If Paula hadn't been pregnant... She hadn't been able to handle that. She had cried, making her eyes ugly and red, and he had become exasperated. In the end she had fled to the bedroom, packed a bag, and told him he could have his divorce, have the apartment, have anything he wanted. Then she had just climbed into her car and driven off.

She had had no clear idea of where she was going. It wasn't until she had found herself driving around the M25, the orbital motorway around London, for the second time, that she had given that problem any consideration. And then she had thought of the cottage out in the wilds of Norfolk, left to her by her great-aunt Floss a couple of years before.

She hadn't been there since she was a child, but she remembered that it was remote, on the edge of a tiny village, miles from anywhere. Suddenly that had seemed enormously appealing, and she had set off, with only a vague idea of how far it was to Cottisham.

Through the fine Norfolk drizzle misting the windscreen, a road-sign showed her that the next turn was to her destination, and she took it. The road was dark, but even if it had been daylight she doubted that she would have recognised it—she would have been no more than about ten years old the last time she was here.

What sort of state would the cottage be in? Aunt Floss had died ... oh, it must have been three years' ago. For the first time, she began to consider that the place would probably be in a bit of a mess. The electricity would probably have been turned off, and maybe even the water too. But at least she was nearly there—she could just go straight to bed tonight, and sort out any problems in the morning.

Her hand found the cigarette-lighter at last, and she flicked it into flame, bending her head to draw deeply on the tobacco...

The headlights came out of nowhere, straight towards her, and too late she realised that the road bent away sharply to the left. In an instinct of panic she snatched at the wheel, braking hard, and the tyres lost their grip on the damp road, sliding into a lazy treacherous skid. In front of her, the beam of her own headlights stabbed out into nothingness...

She wasn't dead, then—it couldn't have been as bad as she had thought it was going to be. She had had an image, fleetingly, of the car tipping over some steep incline and rolling over and over, crushing her. But she seemed to be the right way up, though the car was tipped up at an odd angle, and the windscreen was shattered... And someone was asking her if she was all right.

Damn—how was she going to get to the cottage now? And that was blood trickling down her cheek... Suddenly she realised that she was hurt, and started to scream.

'All right—steady. You can't be too badly injured if you can make that sort of noise.' The voice was calm and competent, and he had reached into the car, unfastening her seatbelt, and was running what felt like an expert hand over her body.

'Are you a doctor?' she whispered, looking up to find a pair of intriguing hazel eyes just a few inches above her own.

He laughed drily. 'No, I'm a vet. You don't seem to have done yourself too much harm—which is more than can be said for your car. Do you think you can move?'

'I think so. But my wrist hurts.'

'Show me.'

She held it out to him gingerly, but his examination was so gentle that she hardly felt it. Some part of her mind was incongruously registering the thought that he was one of the most attractive men she had ever seen: thick dark hair, shaggily cut, fell over a high, intelligent forehead, and his face was starkly masculine, with a strong aquiline nose, and a lean, hard jaw.

'Are you really a vet?' she asked curiously.

'Yes—but the principle's pretty much the same,' he reassured her. 'I think you've broken this. If you can get to my car, I'll take you to the hospital.'

'Your car's all right?'

'You didn't hit me—I managed to brake and get out of your way,' he told her, a faintly sardonic inflexion in his voice. 'What happened? Didn't you see the sign for the bend?'

She tried to shake her head, but found it a jarring experience.

'Steady,' he advised. 'You've been pretty badly shaken up. Take it slowly.'

Supporting her with one strong arm around her shoulders, the other holding her injured arm steady, he eased her very gradually from the car. It was crazy, but she found herself leaning on him just a little more than was strictly necessary; it just felt so good to have a man treating her with a little tenderness, a little kindness, after so many years of Colin's indifference.

His car was just a few feet away, slewed across on to the wrong side of the road, and with a small stab of horror she realised just how dangerously close she had come to a much more serious accident. That thought made her feel slightly sick, and she found that she really did need all his support to make it the short distance to his car.

Dimly she took in that it was an old Land Rover: of course—he would need a tough car if he was a vet. An elderly black and white border collie was sitting in the front seat, but he gave it a crisp order, and with a look of mild indignation at being banished it skipped over into the back.

It was a relief to be able to collapse into the front seat. She closed her eyes, for a few moments conscious only of the fires of pain in her wrist and her head. But she had had a very lucky escape. Opening her eyes, she peered across at her own car.

Well, she had certainly made a mess of that! It was tail-up in a ditch, the bonnet crumpled and the off-side badly smashed in. It was probably going to be a complete insurance write-off. Well, that was Colin's problem, she reflected with vicious satisfaction—both the car and the insurance were in his name.

Her rescuer had placed a warning triangle in front of the wreck to alert any oncoming cars, and was coming back with her suitcase and her handbag. She offered him a grateful smile—but what she really needed was something to steady her nerves.

'Did you bring my cigarettes?' she pleaded urgently.

'Your cigarettes?' The impatient frown that crossed his brow warned her that he didn't much approve of the habit.

'They were on the dashboard...' guiltily she remembered that it had been in lighting a cigarette that she had taken her eyes off the road for just that fatal fraction of a second '...and my lighter,' she begged. 'It might have fallen down.'

'All right,' he conceded grudgingly. 'I'll get them.'

Josey watched him walk back to her car, registering the easy, athletic stride, and the impressive breadth of shoulder beneath his green oiled-cotton jacket. She found herself wishing she hadn't asked him to fetch her cigarettes—he had made her feel about two inches tall, as if she hadn't felt bad enough already. If only she had been able to give up the disgusting things. Somehow—foolishly—it mattered to her what he thought of her.

Not that he was going to think much anyway, she reminded herself miserably. The glass of the Land Rover's windscreen reflected her face to her all too clearly. She looked awful; correction—even more awful than usual. Her eyes were hollow and puffy from crying, and now there was a nice graze on her forehead, still trickling blood. She sought in her handbag for a tissue to dab it away as he came back.

He swung himself behind the steering-wheel, tossing her cigarettes and lighter into her lap, making no effort to conceal his contempt. 'No, I don't mind if you smoke in my car—just this once,' he grated, pre-empting her routinely polite enquiry as if he had doubted whether she would have the manners to ask.

'Thank you,' she mumbled, clumsily trying to open the packet with her one good hand. Tears of frustration welled into her eyes.

'Oh, here, give them to me,' he snapped, taking them from her. He drew one cigarette from the packet and put it between her lips, and then flicked the lighter for her. 'You seem pretty determined to kill yourself, one way or another.'

She stared up at him in shock. 'I wasn't trying to kill myself,' she protested.

'Weren't you?' he queried drily, starting up the Land Rover. 'It was pretty suicidal, the way you were driving.'

'I...had things on my mind.' She looked down into her lap. Just at the moment she didn't feel like telling anyone about her marital problems—least of all this man. He already thought she was a pretty pathetic specimen.

'What were you doing on this road anyway?' he enquired. 'Were you lost?'

'No. I was heading for the village.'

'Cottisham? At this time of night?'

'I was left a cottage there, by my aunt,' she explained. 'I was going to stay there for a . . . a holiday.'

He slanted her a look of surprise. 'You don't mean old Florrie Calder's place?'

'Do you know it?' she asked.

He laughed with sardonic humour. 'Yes, I do. If you were planning to stay there, it's a pity you didn't do something about it before—the place is practically derelict.'

'Derelict? Oh, dear . . . I didn't realise . . .'

'How many years is it since you bothered to visit the old lady?' he enquired, a hard edge in his voice.

'I haven't been up since I was a little girl,' she countered defensively. 'She was my mother's aunt, really, and my mother died when I was twelve.'

'She was all on her own. Don't you think you could have taken a little more interest in her welfare?'

She hung her head, feeling ashamed. He was perfectly right—but it had simply never occurred to her to keep in touch. Even her mother had never been particularly close to the rather eccentric old lady, and after she had died . . . to be honest she had virtually forgotten her existence, until the letter had come from the solicitor informing her that she had been left the cottage. At the time even that had been of little interest—as Colin had said, it was really not very well located for a holiday home.

'I . . . I never thought . . .' she mumbled.

'No, I don't suppose you did.' His tone implied that he would have expected no better of her. Turning his attention impatiently away from her, he pulled over for a moment, reached down and switched on the car-phone. First he called the hospital and warned them of their arrival, then he dialled another number. A woman's voice answered. 'Hello, Maggie,' he said. 'It's Tom. Look, I'm sorry—I'm ringing to let you know I've been delayed. There was a bit of an accident on the road, and I'm running someone to the hospital. I'll get to you as soon as I can.'

'Oh . . . Right,' came the steady response. 'Thank you for letting me know, Tom.'

So who was Maggie? Josey wondered dully. His wife? She had sounded as if it was a regular occurrence for him to be held up by something or other. It must take a great deal of patience to be the wife of a country vet, she reflected—always on call, never knowing when he would have to go out or when he would be back. She would have to be a remarkably strong woman.

She felt a twinge of envy as her imagination began to paint a picture—of a warm, rambling cottage, with the elderly collie snoozing beside the hearth, and a couple of fine strapping sons who took after their father...

They had set off again. Her head was beginning to ache quite badly, and she felt as if she would have liked to cry. Today had very definitely been the worst day of her whole life.

'Is there anyone you want to get in touch with, to let them know you're all right?' he asked, his voice suddenly gentle.

'No.' One single tear escaped from the corner of her eye, and began to track slowly down her cheek. She brushed it away with her good hand. 'Thank you—you've been very kind.'

'You're in shock,' he said. 'Don't worry—we'll be at the hospital in a couple of minutes.'

She nodded gratefully. It would be nice to be able to lie down, and have someone take away the pain. But a strange pang of regret tugged at her heart—once he had deposited her at the hospital, Tom would go away, and she wouldn't see him again. He probably wouldn't even spare her another thought, except as the crazy woman who had almost smashed into his car.

Stupid, she scolded herself crossly. The last thing she needed at the moment was to start fancying she was attracted to some total stranger, who had crossed her path by complete chance. And yet . . . he *was* very attractive, she conceded, slanting him a covert glance from beneath her lashes. Six feet plus of rangy, well-built male, the kind that no woman could ignore.

And his hands . . . They were beautiful, with long, sensitive fingers, and strong wrists. She found herself remembering the gentle way those hands had examined her, and a shimmer of heat ran through her . . .

No—it was all just reaction. The shock of Colin's announcement, followed by the accident, had left her off balance. And he was so very different from Colin—Colin with his immaculately combed hair, his designer suits, his decaffeinated coffee. She couldn't imagine this man drinking decaffeinated coffee. He wouldn't need to fuss with such things, not with the healthy, active life he must lead. So very different . . .

It was pleasant, this feeling of being close to him, cocooned in the warmth of the car—like some comfortable dream from which she never wanted to wake up . . .

'Here we are.'

She opened her eyes quickly to find that he had brought the car to a halt beside a wide porch, with a pair of battered plastic swing doors of the type used so much in hospitals. A sign above the entrance said ACCIDENT AND EMERGENCY. A young nurse had come out to the car, bringing a wheelchair.

'I don't need a chair,' Josey mumbled, feeling guilty for causing such a lot of fuss.

'Better if you do,' Tom insisted firmly, climbing out of the Land Rover and coming round to help her out.

And indeed she found that she did. During the short drive her body seemed to have stiffened; she could hardly move, and as he helped her gently to her feet her head swam sickeningly. She dropped heavily into the chair, and half closed her eyes again.

With part of her mind she was conscious of the nurse flirting with him somewhere above her head, but she was past caring. They wheeled her into a small reception area, and straight over to a narrow cubicle, curtained with some ancient flowered cotton.

'Could you just pop up on the trolley?' asked the nurse, gratingly bright.

She looked round for Tom, but he had gone—and he hadn't even said goodbye. But then she heard his voice on the other side of the curtain. 'Hello, Andy.'

'Well, hello, Tom. What's going on? You don't have enough of your own kind of patients, so you've had to start poaching mine?'

Tom laughed; he had a nice laugh, Josey decided— low and sort of husky, from spending so much time out in the raw Norfolk air. 'No—just some woman who ran her car into a ditch.' His tone was casually dismissive. 'I don't think it's too serious—fortunately she had her seatbelt on. I think you'll find she's broken a bone in her wrist, but apart from that she's just generally a bit bruised and battered.'

'Any sign of concussion?'

'No, just shock.'

'Fine. Well, I'd better take a look at her.'

The curtain was brushed briskly aside, and the doctor came in. 'Well, now, what have you done to yourself?' he asked pleasantly, bending over the trolley.

'It's...just my wrist,' she managed to respond. She could just see Tom, through the half-open curtain, chatting to the nurse again. A stab of stupid jealousy shot through her. The girl was pretty, with a mass of sexily luxuriant ash-blonde hair, tucked up neatly beneath her white cap, and an expression of sweet feminine kindliness. It was a combination that most men would find devastating.

Was he married? Maybe not, after all—maybe the nurse was his girlfriend. In fact, she wouldn't mind betting that every unattached female in the district under the age of sixty was after him. Forget it, she advised herself despondently. Maybe once, a few years ago, she could have stood a chance of competing, but not now—he wouldn't even look twice.

Wearily she closed her eyes, hardly interested in what was happening to her as the doctor examined her. His touch was light, but not quite as gentle as Tom's had been, and Josey found herself wishing that it were he who was examining her instead.

'Well, I don't think you've done yourself any serious injury, apart from your wrist,' the doctor was saying. 'I'll send you down for an X-ray on that, and then we'd better see about putting it in plaster for you.'

She nodded apathetically. Tom had gone, and she just wished they would let her go to sleep. But first the nurse had a form to fill in, with all her personal details, and then a porter came—the irritatingly cheerful sort—and wheeled her through deserted corridors to the X-ray department. Then at last it was back to Casualty, where someone put a warm plastic splint on her wrist, and tied it up in a sling.

She was back in her cubicle, half-dozing in the wheelchair, when she heard Tom's voice outside again. 'I thought I'd just drop by on my way home and see how she is.'

'She seems fine,' the doctor responded, a note of constraint in his voice. 'There's no sign of concussion. The wrist is fractured, but it's been set. Apart from a bit of shock, there are no other problems.'

'So what's wrong?'

She heard the doctor sigh. 'I really can't justify keeping her in, Tom—not on medical grounds. You know the situation we're in for beds—I've got a threatened miscarriage in cubicle three, and I've already had to send a coronary over to the Norwich.'

'You're going to discharge her?' He sounded surprised.

'I don't really have much choice. At the most, I suppose I could stretch a point and keep her here until the morning. But all she needs is a couple of days' rest, with someone to keep an eye on her, and she'll be perfectly all right. Did she mention to you where she was planning to stay? Does she have friends or relatives up here?'

Josey heard Tom laugh drily. 'She was old Miss Calder's niece—remember that old stone cottage out by Breck's Coppice?'

'She wasn't planning to stay there?' The doctor sounded incredulous. 'But it's been empty for years— it must be practically falling down!'

'Oh, the structure's basically quite sound, but it'll need a lot doing to it to make it habitable. Though she looks as if she's got the money,' he added, a sardonic inflexion in his voice. 'Anyone who can afford to write off a Porsche can't be short of a bob or two.'

There was a distinct note of contempt in his voice, and Josey felt herself wishing she could crawl into a corner. Of course those who eavesdropped never heard good of themselves, she reflected bitterly, but what else could she do but listen?

'But in the meantime, that doesn't solve my problem of what to do with her, does it?' the doctor pointed out grimly. 'Of course, I could ring her husband and get him to come and fetch her.'

'No!' The sharp protest broke involuntarily from Josey's lips, and she tried to stand up.

The curtain was drawn back, and the doctor hurried in, frowning as he saw her struggling to her feet. 'Now, now! You shouldn't be trying to get up on your own,' he chided, pushing her back with a gentle pressure that Josey didn't have the strength to resist.

'There's . . . no need to ring my husband,' she insisted weakly. 'I'll find myself a hotel or something.'

Tom had come in behind the doctor, and he laughed mockingly at her words. 'Where do you think you are, South Kensington?' he enquired drily. 'We don't have too many hotels around here, and those there are will be full for the tourist season.'

'Besides, I wouldn't be very happy just to let you go to a hotel,' the doctor put in seriously. 'Don't you have anyone up here you could go to for a few days? A relative, or a friend?'

'No,' she admitted reluctantly. 'It's years since I've been up here. It . . . it was just an impulse that I came, really.'

The doctor sighed. 'Well, where are you going to go . . .?' He hesitated, glancing round at Tom. 'I don't suppose . . .?'

Tom looked faintly alarmed. 'What . . .?'

'It would only be for a day or two,' the doctor assured him persuasively. 'She won't need any special care—just lots of rest. By Monday she should be as right as rain.'

Josey gasped in shock as she realised what the doctor was suggesting. 'Oh, no! I couldn't possibly...!'

'It would really be an enormous help, Tom,' the doctor persisted. 'Besides, if I knew it was you keeping an eye on her, I'd know she was all right.'

Tom hesitated, then smiled wryly. 'OK,' he conceded with no great deal of enthusiasm. 'It looks as if that's the only option.'

The doctor looked relieved. 'I'll give you a prescription for some diazepam for her—the pharmacy will be able to make it up for you tomorrow. Where have you parked your car? Nurse, get the porter to bring a chair, will you?'

He bustled away without waiting for an answer, leaving Josey looking up at Tom in some embarrassment. 'I'm sorry,' she murmured awkwardly. 'I've put you to so much inconvenience already.'

'It's no trouble.' But his unsmiling expression did nothing to reassure her.

'I'll find a hotel as...as soon as I can.'

'I said it's no trouble,' he reiterated a little impatiently. 'Just don't expect the Ritz.'

CHAPTER TWO

JOSEY lay in the big bed with her eyes open, trying to make herself believe that all this was actually real. Bright sunlight streamed through yellow chintz curtains, falling on the faded home-made patchwork that covered her bed and warming the mellow oak of the old-fashioned furniture.

Yesterday morning, and most other mornings for years past, she had woken in a stylish Italian bed, in a room with smart white walls and a pale beech floor, where she could just glimpse the south column of Tower Bridge if she leaned slightly to her left. Colin would be in the shower, and she would pad out of bed and into their glossy space-age kitchen, to pour him a glass of orange juice from a carton in the refrigerator.

But yesterday had gone—irrevocably. Her marriage—or rather the empty shell of it that she had been clinging to as if it were some kind of security blanket for so long—was over, and she had to face the world on her own. And this world was very different from any she would have expected to find herself in.

She didn't remember much about getting here from the hospital. The doctor had injected her with some kind of pain-killer, and she had wanted to do nothing but sleep. She vaguely recalled a low, rambling building of weathered brick and flint, and the perfume of roses on the night air. And a cosy, old-fashioned kitchen, with a slightly uneven quarry-tiled floor, and a wicker dog-basket with a well-chewed red blanket beside a large inglenook fireplace.

These images came back to her like snap-shots in her mind. She could remember too, with a feeling that made her mouth a little dry, how she had stumbled woozily, and Tom had picked her up as if she weighed nothing at all, and carried her up a flight of steep, narrow stairs, and brought her into this room, with its low, oak-beamed ceiling and big comfortable bed.

And she had been so clumsy with her wrist splinted and tied up in a sling that she had had considerable trouble getting out of her clothes and into her night-dress, and he had had to come and help her. But the unceremonious way he had dealt with the task had told her quite unmistakably that any modesty on her part would have been quite wasted—she held absolutely no allure for him whatsoever.

What she didn't remember, though it was the one thing she had been trying to look for, was anything that suggested the presence of a wife or children in the house. She had only the impression of an exclusively male atmosphere—the shelf above the fireplace was merely a convenient place to put anything that didn't have an immediate home, none of the roses from the garden had found their way indoors, and the curtains were purely functional and slightly in need of a wash.

With a wry smile she acknowledged to herself that such interest in the details of his domestic arrangements was really rather silly. But maybe she just needed a shred of romantic fantasy, to cushion the shock of the abrupt ending of her marriage. And maybe she was looking to him for just the smallest reassurance that she might still have some attraction for a man because it was so long since Colin had shown the least interest in her.

With a sigh she eased herself gingerly up on the pillows. If it was flattery she was seeking, she was wasting her time with Tom Quinn. Maybe he reserved all his warmth for the animals he cared for—he seemed to have little to spare for the human species, or at least for the female half of it.

But then what did she expect? Maybe five or six years ago she might have been able to make some impression, but she was going to have to take herself seriously in hand if she was ever going to expect any man to be attracted to her again. If it wasn't already too late; she was getting dangerously close to her sell-by date.

Goodness, she felt stiff. Every inch of her body ached, her head was sore, and her wrist was both throbbing and numb at the same time. And she was dying for a cigarette. Forming the thought brought the familiar craving, and she knew that somehow she was going to have to get out of bed to reach the packet, which was on the dressing-table on the far side of the room.

Tears of self-pity rose to her eyes. It was an exhausting effort even to move, and the dressing-table seemed a hundred miles away. But that raw need wouldn't let her have any peace. Tossing aside the quilted bedcover with an exclamation of impatience, she swung herself round and put her feet on the floor.

Dark pain swam before her eyes, and she had to wait a moment for it to clear. Then gritting her teeth she tried to stand up. She had managed about three steps when the door opened, and Tom appeared on the threshold, a breakfast tray in his hands.

'What the devil are you doing getting out of bed on your own?' he demanded brusquely.

'I...I was trying to get my cigarettes,' she explained, giving up and sinking back on to the bed.

'Why didn't you call me?'

'I thought...you'd probably be busy or something,' she mumbled. Suddenly she was all too acutely aware of the way the dipping neckline of her silk nightdress revealed the gaunt hollows of her shoulders, while the pale ivory colour did absolutely nothing for her washed-out complexion. She crawled back under the bedclothes, drawing them up over her. 'I'm sorry.'

A flicker of impatience crossed his face. 'You don't have to keep apologising,' he grated, setting the tray down on a low pine chest beside the bed. He moved across and picked up the cigarettes, tossing them on to the bed with undisguised contempt. 'Eat your breakfast,' he advised tersely. 'It'll do you more good than those things.'

'I...I don't know if I can eat very much,' she stumbled, eyeing the laden tray without appetite. 'I don't usually have breakfast.'

'No.' The wry twist of his mouth conveyed what he didn't actually say—that she was too thin. He stood looking down at her in critical appraisal as she lit her cigarette, drawing on it deeply in relief. 'How many of those do you smoke a day?' he asked bluntly.

'Oh...only about twenty or so.' She shrugged, unable to meet his eyes. 'I know they're no good for me, and I've tried giving them up, but I just can't.'

'You could if you wanted to.'

She slanted him a resentful look from beneath her lashes. It was easy enough for him to say that—he'd probably never smoked. He didn't look the sort of man who had ever suffered from a lack of will-power. 'Yes, well...I'll give them up some time,' she promised vaguely. 'But not just at the moment—they say you shouldn't try to give up when you're under stress.'

'That's the best time to do it,' he persisted with ruthless insistence. 'If you can cope without them now, you'll be able to cope without them any time.'

Those stupid tears were stinging the backs of her eyes again. 'I'm sorry,' she mumbled thickly, and then, remembering that he had told her not to keep saying she was sorry, she apologised for that too. 'I'm sorry.'

He laughed drily. 'Eat your breakfast,' he repeated, and went out, closing the door behind him.

Josey leaned back against the pillows, closing her eyes. How had she ever let herself sink into such a mess, that she couldn't start the day without a cigarette? It was no wonder that Tom treated her with such disdain.

Wearily she turned to the breakfast tray he had brought her. There was far more food than she could ever manage, even if she had been feeling more like her usual self. With a groan she realised that she wouldn't be able to manage half of it—and Tom was going to be even more annoyed with her.

He had every right to be, of course—she had been nothing but a nuisance to him since she had all but smashed up his car last night. It would be better if she just took herself off to a hotel somewhere, out of his way. Holding that thought resolutely in her mind, she rolled herself painfully out of bed.

There was a small sink in the corner of the room, and she dragged herself over to it and had a sketchy wash, and then with some considerable difficulty got dressed. She had just finished, and was struggling one-handed to re-fasten her suitcase when Tom came back into the room.

'What do you think you're doing now?' he demanded. 'I told you not to try getting out of bed on your own—and you haven't even touched your breakfast.'

'I know—I'm sorry.' Damn—he had told her not to keep saying that. 'You've been very kind to me, and I'm very grateful, but I can't trespass on your hospitality any longer. If I could just use your telephone, I'll ring for a taxi, and find a hotel somewhere.'

'Don't be silly,' he rapped, his patience strained. 'You're as weak as a kitten. Get back into bed.'

'No—I'm leaving,' she insisted, though already just the effort of getting dressed and packing her bag had left her feeling exhausted. 'I'm just a nuisance—you don't want me here . . .' Oh, damn—why did her voice have to waver so pathetically? She tried to pick up her suitcase, but it was loaded with bricks, and she slumped to her knees, tears of frustration stinging her eyes.

'Get back into bed,' he repeated, the sudden gentleness in his voice so unexpected that it made her sob harder. 'You're in no fit state to go anywhere today.' His strong arms came around her, helping her to her feet, and he led her over to the bed, sitting down beside her, still holding her comfortingly close. 'I'm sorry if I've made you feel so unwelcome.' The taut note in his voice made her wonder just how rare it was for him to apologise. 'I suppose I'm more used to four-legged patients than two-legged ones.'

'I'm sorry,' she mumbled, her mind half-drugged by the evocative male muskiness of his skin. 'I must be in your way. You've got work to do, and I'm taking up your time, running around after me, making my breakfast...'

'Vi made your breakfast,' he corrected her drily. 'She couldn't bring it up herself—she's got a touch of arthritis, and can't manage the stairs.'

'Oh...' She managed to stifle her tears, helped by a strong dose of curiosity. It didn't seem very likely that this Vi was his wife, if she was old enough to suffer from arthritis. 'Who's Vi?' she asked, trying to sound as if she had no more than a casual interest.

'My housekeeper.'

'Oh.' She flickered him a cautious glance from beneath her lashes. 'You're... not married then?'

'No.'

'So... who was Maggie?'

'Maggie?' He looked faintly puzzled. 'Oh, you mean Maggie Hunter? She's the wife of a farmer over by Saltham Marsh. I was on my way to look at one of their cows when we—er—ran into each other.'

'Oh...' She could feel a faint blush of pink colouring her cheeks. Had she revealed a bit too much by asking such a pointed question?

He reached out and took the bowl of cereal from the tray, putting it into her hands. 'Come on—just try and eat some of this,' he coaxed. 'You'll feel a lot better with some good food inside you.'

She doubted it, but she made the effort just to please him—and rather to her surprise she was able to eat most of the contents of the bowl.

'That's better,' he approved. 'Don't worry about the rest—maybe you'll be able to eat a little more later.' He glanced at his watch. 'Now that you're dressed, you might as well come downstairs and rest on the settee. I have to go out, but at least it'll be a bit more interesting for you than being stuck up here with nothing to do.'

'Thank you.' She managed to smile, though it was rather a weak effort. 'You've been very kind.'

He smiled back at her—and her heart flipped over. It was the first time she had seen him smile, and it was like the sun coming out, transforming his hard features at a stroke. 'Some people would say that kindness isn't my strong point,' he remarked with an inflexion of sardonic humour. 'At least as far as human beings are concerned.'

'Oh, no,' she protested a little breathlessly. 'You've done so much for me.'

'Yes, well ... You don't have to keep thanking me,' he grated, that terseness back in his voice, as if he found her thanks even more irksome than her presence. 'Come on, I'll help you downstairs. Can you walk, or shall I carry you?'

'Oh, no—I can walk.' The thought of being scooped up in those strong arms again was enough to make her heart thud. Really, it was plain ridiculous, she scolded herself. She was reacting like a schoolgirl, not a sensible married woman of thirty-one. Just because he was so good-looking ...

And he was. It was no use telling herself that it was simply the circumstances that were making her more than usually vulnerable. She had never even reacted to Colin like this. And the danger was that the powerful tug of physical attraction she was feeling was undermining her common sense, luring her into building all sorts of stupid romantic fantasies about him—especially now she knew that he wasn't married.

But she must be very careful not to give herself away, she reminded herself firmly. He most certainly wouldn't appreciate it.

The kitchen was the main room of the house. It had that old-fashioned country feel about it that interior designers were always trying to recreate, and never could. No one could reproduce the comfort of the huge sofa that she was lying on, with old Jethro curled up in the crook of her knees, nor capture the feeling of sunshine streaming through a window on to white-washed brick walls.

Last night she hadn't paid much attention to the location of the house, but it seemed to be in the middle of the village, and people were passing by outside all the time, calling to each other in greeting. Dogs barked occasionally; a rumbling farm tractor had gone past twice, the second time leaving a waft of rich country air in its wake; a couple of horses had clattered by; somewhere close to the window she could hear a bird singing.

Josey had wondered what Vi would think of a strange woman turning up in Tom's house in the middle of the night, but that lady had been kindness itself. From the minute Josey had come downstairs she had fussed over her, making her comfortable with piles of soft cushions and bringing through some battered old magazines from the waiting-room of Tom's surgery for her to read.

Before she had left, she had insisted on bringing her a cup of strong tea, and a thick wedge of moist dark fruit-cake, home-baked. It was years since she had eaten home-baked cake—her mother had always used to make cakes on Fridays for the weekend, and she had learned herself, but Colin never ate cake, and so it had never seemed worth bothering.

But this was delicious. Jethro lifted his head, sniffing hopefully at her hand, hinting that perhaps she might like to share her good fortune with a friend. She stroked his sleek head, laughing.

'Are you allowed tit-bits like this?' she asked him. 'I'm not sure that cake's very good for you.' His liquid eyes—so like his master's—gazed at her meltingly, and she could not be immune. 'All right,' she conceded, breaking off a small piece and holding it out for him. 'But don't tell.'

The telephone began to ring, but she ignored it. Vi had told her that the answering service would cut in, and after a moment it did. With a sigh she laid her head back on the cushions, and closed her eyes. Sooner or later she was going to have to ring Colin, and let him know about the accident, and where she was. But not yet.

The clicking of the latch on the front door brought her awake as she was beginning to slide away into sleep again, and she lifted her head, expecting Tom. But Jethro clearly didn't—there was no bark of welcome. He simply shifted his head, turning it away from the door in a manner of bored contempt.

The woman who appeared in the doorway was about the same age as Josey herself, a willowy blonde with the fine bone-structure and peaches-and-cream complexion of the English upper classes. Her white kid jodhpurs and leather riding-whip gave the same impression, and her voice had the cut-glass diction of the county set.

'Oh...' She regarded Josey with refined astonishment, rather as if she were something naughty the Labrador had done on the carpet. 'I called to see Tom.'

That haughty manner made Josey's hackles rise. 'He's out,' she responded, deliberately unhelpful.

'I see...'

Josey felt the sharp scrutiny of those ice-blue eyes, missing nothing, and sensed a hostility that was a little puzzling—unless this young madam regarded the local vet as her personal property, and resented the interloper. 'Can I give him a message?' she enquired, cuttingly polite.

'Oh... No, it's all right. I thought perhaps Zella had thrown a spavin, but it's probably nothing. I'll walk her home gently, and if that doesn't do the trick I'll call him out later.'

The smile was confident enough, but the voice held just a hint of uncertainty. It had clearly unsettled her to find another woman ensconced in Tom's kitchen, apparently very much at home. And Jethro, bless him, decided at that moment to start licking Josey's hand, as if to demonstrate a bond of deep affection.

'Fine—I'll tell him you called,' she responded casually.

So who was that? she wondered as the door closed behind the visitor. A proper little lady of the manor— was she a regular girlfriend of Tom's? But clearly, in spite of the impression she had tried to give, she wasn't quite sure of him—and that gave Josey a kind of perverse satisfaction.

But of course it was all just a daydream. She would only be here for a few days—as soon as she was well enough, she would be leaving. Besides, he wasn't remotely attracted to her anyway—he had made that more than clear.

Automatically her hand reached out for her cigarettes, but then with a muttered curse she remembered that she had smoked the last one half an hour ago. She had known that she was running short, but she hadn't liked to ask Tom to buy some for her.

But now she was beginning to feel that uncomfortable craving. How far was it to a shop that might sell cigarettes? It was so frustrating to feel so weak—even to think of walking a hundred yards made her want to cry with exhaustion. And first she would have to get upstairs to her bedroom to fetch her purse.

If only she could give the horrible things up. She knew the unpleasant smell of tobacco smoke clung to her hair and clothes, and she had lately noticed that her teeth were starting to turn yellow from the nicotine. And she had read somewhere that smoking caused the skin to age prematurely—she'd used to have good skin. But she *needed* a smoke—needed it as a starving man needed food.

The stairs seemed like Mount Everest, but with grim determination she managed to climb them. She had to sit down on the edge of the bed to recover, and at that moment the sound of a car drawing up beside the house came to her ears, and from Jethro's excited barking she guessed that it was Tom. Damn, why did he have to come back *now*, and catch her?

She heard him come in, and speak a few words to Jethro, and then he was coming up the stairs two at a time. She rose to her feet, ready to confront him, feeling as guilty as a naughty schoolgirl—though she knew she had every right to go out and buy herself a packet of cigarettes if she wished to.

On the threshold he paused, a look of angry impatience crossing his face. 'What are you doing up here?' he demanded.

'I . . . I'm sorry.' Automatically she was apologising again. 'I didn't mean . . . I just came up to——'

'You shouldn't be climbing the stairs when there's no one in the house,' he grated. 'What if you'd fallen?'

Her temper—strained by the nicotine craving—was close to snapping. 'All right—I'm not completely stupid, you know,' she retorted tartly. 'If I'd thought I might fall, I wouldn't have tried it.'

The sharpness of her response had startled her as much as it did him, and as he frowned at her she sighed inwardly, waiting for him to bite her head off. But instead, quite unexpectedly, that incredible smile unfurled. 'I'm sorry,' he conceded wryly. 'I was just worried—you should be resting.'

She couldn't quite meet his eyes, conscious that her cheeks were tinged a delicate shade of pink. 'I . . . I've been resting all day,' she managed, trying hard to keep her voice steady. 'I ought to be ready for a five-mile run.'

A little stiffly, she rose to her feet. She would go without the damned cigarettes now. Maybe he was right—if she could manage to give them up when she was at such a low ebb, she would never need them again. 'Oh . . . by the way,' she added, slanting him a covert look from beneath her lashes, 'there was a woman here to see you a little while ago. Something about her horse. She said she might call you later.'

'She didn't leave a name?'

'No. She . . . seemed to think you would know who it was.'

A flicker of some expression passed across his eyes, but it was gone too quickly for her to read it. 'I see,' was all he said.

Having asserted that she was sure she wouldn't fall, she was alarmed by how dizzy she felt as she gazed down the steep flight of stairs. But she wasn't going to let him see that—he might offer to carry her again. Resolutely gritting her teeth, she took hold of the banister and slowly made her way down.

It was quite a relief to get back to the settee. She sank down a little more heavily than she had intended, leaning back and closing her eyes. It was hard to believe that just that small amount of effort could be so exhausting. Beside her she heard Tom laugh drily.

'You're not quite as fit as you think you are, are you?' he remarked, a sardonic glint in his eyes.

'No, I'm not,' she conceded. 'I feel perfectly all right when I'm sitting down, but when I try to move around it catches up with me.'

'You'll be better in a day or two,' he assured her, his voice surprisingly gentle. 'I'm just going to put the kettle on. Would you like a cup of coffee?'

'Y-yes, please.' It made her nervous when he was being kind to her—it felt much safer when he was shouting.

Why did he have to be so utterly gorgeous? Averagely good-looking she could have coped with, but in her present highly susceptible state this just wasn't fair.

She watched him covertly from beneath her lashes as he made the coffee, fascinated by every economical movement.

There was something so very self-sufficient about him; he was a man who didn't need a woman around. He had Vi to take care of his domestic comfort, and probably a whole posse of willing young ladies to minister to his other needs, without ever being offered much in the way of commitment. He got all the close companionship he needed from his dog.

But, though he wasn't married now, had he been once? She judged him to be maybe in his middle thirties—surely even he hadn't been able to get off scot-free all these years? There were so many things she wanted to know about him, but she guessed that he wouldn't easily be persuaded to talk about himself.

He brought her coffee, and then folded himself into the battered old armchair beside the fireplace, his long, lean legs sprawled across the stone hearth. Jethro collapsed in a bundle at his feet, his head draped over his ankles, his eyes closed in sheer bliss.

Josey sipped her coffee, searching her mind for something to say, simply to make conversation. 'This is a nice cottage,' she remarked, trying to keep her tone light and casual. 'Have you lived here long?'

'It was my uncle's place. We were partners for a while, but he retired about five years ago—though he still comes in to help with the small animal clinic a couple of afternoons a week.'

'You . . . were born around here, then?' she asked.

He nodded. 'My parents have got a farm, over by Withingham. Cows, mostly, and a few pigs. But my brother does most of the work now—he's the farmer out of the two of us. My father's nearly seventy—though he insists he isn't quite ready to retire yet!'

His tone was quite friendly, and, emboldened, she risked probing a little further. 'Had you always wanted to be a vet?'

'Ever since I was a kid,' he responded with a grin. 'I was always over here, pestering my uncle to let me help him. I used to drive him mad, bringing in birds that had broken a wing, or a rabbit I'd let out of a farmer's gin-trap. That didn't make me very popular in certain quarters, either,' he added darkly. 'Sometimes I think that, the more I know about people, the more I prefer animals.'

'It must be hard work,' she mused.

He laughed drily. 'Yes, it is—damned hard work, and there's no money in it.' He slanted her a look of hard mockery. 'Not the sort of money that would run to a Porsche, anyway.'

She blinked in shock—that gibe had stung.

'So what sort of work did you do in London?' he persisted, a cynical edge in his voice, as if he was expecting something totally frivolous.

'Oh, I...used to be a secretary,' she stumbled. 'But I haven't worked for several years now. My...husband didn't want me to.'

'How long have you been married?'

'Nearly nine years. A long time, isn't it? You can get less than that for murder these days.'

He lifted one dark eyebrow in sardonic enquiry. 'It seemed like a prison sentence?'

'Worse!' She was unable to keep the bitterness from her laugh. 'At least with a prison sentence you get time off for good behaviour!'

'But on the other hand, you wouldn't get to serve your sentence in some posh Docklands penthouse, or drive around in a flash sports car,' he pointed out with a touch of asperity.

She flashed him a look of angry indignation. 'What do you mean?'

'Well, you weren't exactly in a hurry to leave, were you?' he taunted.

'Well, no... but I——'

'Nine years—was it worth it for all that comfortable lifestyle?' he sneered. 'The clothes, and the jewellery, and the fast cars...'

'That's not true!' she protested, stung. 'How can you judge me? You don't even know me.'

'I don't need to know you—I just have to look at you.' His eyes lashed her with icy disdain. 'What is it they say—"You can never be too rich or too thin"? You've dieted so much to fit the fashionable image you're practically a bag of bones, and you're so screwed-up you can't get by without those things.' He cast a contemptuous glance at the empty cigarette packet on the table beside her. 'I'll tell you something—if you put on a bit of weight you might look halfway decent, but until you sort out what's going on in your head, you'll never——'

His words were interrupted by a sharp ring at the doorbell. He rose swiftly to his feet and crossed the room, to admit a tall, ruddy-faced young man, still in his muddy wellington boots. In his arms he was carrying a drooping bundle, wrapped in an old blanket.

'I'm sorry to barge in like this, Tom—I know it ain't your surgery tonight. But it's our old Shep,' he blurted out, agitated and upset. 'He was perfectly all right this morning, but when the missus came in from fetching the kiddies from school he was like this— couldn't move, couldn't get up, wasn't even interested in his bone. Daft old mutt, he is, and getting on a bit now, but the kids love him. I don't know if there's anything you can do.'

'That's fine, Bob,' Tom assured him swiftly. 'Bring him through to the clinic.'

'Do you . . . think he's going to be all right?'

Tom hesitated, casting a doubtful eye at the bundle in the young farmer's arms. 'I'll do my best,' he promised.

CHAPTER THREE

DRAWN by an instinctive concern for the little dog, Josey followed them. The veterinary clinic was through a thick oak door at the end of the passage. A cluttered office led into a much larger room, with a rubber-topped table in the middle of it and all manner of important-looking equipment stowed neatly around the walls.

'Put him down, Bob,' Tom instructed, gesturing towards the table. 'You get off home now—I'll have a look at him, and see what I can do.'

'Right.' The farmer's voice was suspiciously thickened, and Josey noticed him surreptitiously wipe a tear from the corner of his eye. 'Well, I'll leave you to it, then. Maybe I'll give you a ring in a couple of hours to see what's what.' Reluctantly he turned away from the table, barely even noticing Josey as he stepped past her.

She moved over to the table. The dog was a medium-sized black and white mongrel, with thick shaggy fur and a tail just made to be wagged. But now he was still, and even Josey could see that he was tense with pain. 'Do you think he'll be all right?' she asked, unconsciously echoing the farmer's words.

Tom was bending over his patient, his sensitive fingers gently examining the small, trembling body. 'I don't know,' he admitted wryly. 'I've a nasty feeling he's got peritonitis—maybe from a ruptured appendix or a punctured intestine. I'm going to have to open him up and have a look.'

He didn't sound very hopeful, and Josey felt tears rise to prick the backs of her eyes. Some children were going to be very sad if their pet didn't make it. 'Is there ... anything I can do to help?' she asked.

'Just sit there by his head and keep an eye on him,' he instructed as he deftly slipped a needle into the dog's vein, and hooked it up to a plasma drip. 'I'll have to try and get his fluid balance right before I can operate. Make sure he's breathing steadily, and tell me if the colour of his gums changes.'

She nodded, glad to be able to contribute if only in a token way, and, pulling over a stool, she sat down. 'Come on, Shep,' she coaxed, stroking the small shaggy head. 'Keep fighting, boy. Just think of all those lovely bones waiting for you if you get well.'

As Tom worked, Josey watched, fascinated by the skill in those beautifully made hands. Gone was all trace of that cynical, short-tempered man of so brief a time before; he had turned on the radio, and to the soothing strains of a Rachmaninov violin concerto he was performing the delicate operation on the small furry body that slumbered in anaesthetised bliss on the table.

He seemed so deep in concentration that she was taken by surprise when he sat back. Glancing across at her, he caught the unguarded expression of admiration in her eyes, and a smile of mocking amusement flickered across his face.

'Well, I think that should do it,' he said, flexing the muscles in his wide shoulders to ease their tension. 'How's he looking?'

'Fine,' Josey confirmed, feeling a surge of embarrassed colour in her own cheeks at having betrayed herself. 'Will he be all right now?'

'Well, it's still touch and go, but if Bob hadn't brought him in when he did he wouldn't have stood a chance. We'll know in a few hours whether he's going to pull through. I'll just get him settled in the sick-bay, and then we can see how he gets on over the next couple of hours. Come on, old feller.' Gently he stroked his hand over the dog's shaggy head. 'Just hang in there a bit longer.'

With infinite care, he lifted his small patient and carried him through to a back room. There was already one occupant—a young tabby cat, who hissed viciously to show her resentment of being confined in her cage.

'All right, Tuppence, I know it's time for your dinner,' Tom remarked to her soothingly as he passed.

Against one wall was a low wooden bench, divided into individual pens, and Shep was laid gently on a cosy pad of fibre bedding, his head arranged so that his tongue wouldn't obstruct his breathing. Josey bent to look at him.

'He...he's twitching a bit,' she remarked anxiously. 'Is he all right?'

Tom laughed. 'He's dreaming. He's probably out in a field somewhere, chasing rabbits. That's a good sign—it shows he's starting to come out of the anaesthetic.'

'Oh.' She managed a reasonably steady smile. 'I didn't know dogs dreamed.'

Those intriguing hazel eyes slanted her an enigmatic smile. 'Everybody dreams.'

He was very close to her, and the faint, evocative muskiness of his skin drifted across her senses. She felt her heartbeat accelerate in response, and turned away quickly, afraid that he might pick up signals that she didn't want to transmit.

'Would you . . . would you like a cup of coffee?' she offered, to cover her confusion.

'That seems like a good idea.'

'Right.' She hurried away to the kitchen before he could notice that her cheeks were flushing a deepening pink.

But it proved far from easy to manage the simple task of filling the kettle with only one good hand, and she splashed water all over the place. Then trying to unscrew the lid from the coffee jar, she split the granules all over the scullery floor.

Her overwrought nerves seemed to snap in frustration, and she swore fiercely, tears springing to her eyes. From the doorway came the sound of Tom's laughter, low and husky. 'Having trouble?' he teased gently.

'I couldn't get the lid off. I'm sorry, I . . .' She knew she was dangerously close to making a complete fool of herself.

'Hey . . .!' To her surprise, he came over, and took her gently in his arms, drawing her against him. 'Come on—it isn't that important,' he soothed, stroking his hand over her hair. 'It's only a bit of coffee.'

She couldn't help it—she knew it was meant to be no more than a comforting gesture, but the impact of being held so close to him, feeling the warm strength of his arms around her, breathing the evocative male muskiness of his skin, fuelled the fires of that fantasy she had been dwelling in, and she lifted

her head, her lips softly parted, as if half expecting
him to kiss her.

There was an arrested expression in those deep hazel
eyes, as if he too had been taken by surprise, and for
one timeless moment they hovered in uncertainty...and then with a faintly sardonic smile he let
her go.

'I'd better wipe it up,' he said.

'Oh...no, I'll do that,' she offered quickly, her heart
pounding in painful embarrassment.

'Perhaps you'd better not,' he advised in mocking
amusement. 'You seem to be seriously accident-prone.'

'I'm not usually,' she protested, not liking the
clumsy, incompetent image he seemed to have of her.

'Well, never mind. It's soon done.' He had taken
a floor cloth from beneath the sink, and mopped the
floor quickly. '*I'll* make the coffee.'

She flashed a fulminating glare at his indifferent
back, and sat down at the big scrubbed-pine table.
He had retreated back into those arctic wastes he normally inhabited, and yet...somehow she was sure she
hadn't imagined what she had seen in his eyes just a
moment ago.

Mind, it was so long since a man had looked at her
with any kind of interest that she wasn't sure if she
would even recognise it now, she conceded wryly. But
it *had* seemed, just for those few incredible seconds,
as if he really was going to kiss her...

Impatiently she shook her head. It was dangerous
enough to let herself indulge in stupid romantic fantasies about him, but if she was going to start im-
agining that he might be remotely interested in her she
was going to end up making a complete fool of herself.

By the time he brought the coffee she had managed to reassemble some kind of mask of composure, and her voice was commendably even as she thanked him.

'How's the wrist?' he enquired, sitting down opposite her.

'Oh...not too bad,' she responded with a flickering smile. 'It still hurts a bit.'

'You were extremely lucky,' he reminded her.

'I know.' She risked a brief glance up at him. 'I suppose I ought to report the accident to the police?'

'I've already reported it. Jack'll be down to talk to you about it when you're feeling a bit better.'

'Do you suppose they'll charge me with careless driving?' she asked anxiously.

He shook his head. 'I doubt it. Apart from Bill Wickham's ditch, you were the only one who suffered any damage. You'll need to put in an insurance claim, of course.'

'It's on my husband's insurance.' She couldn't keep the edge of bitterness from her voice. 'Personally I don't give a damn whether he makes a claim or not.'

'Even so, don't you think you'd better ring him and let him know where you are?' he enquired levelly.

'He won't care,' she asserted. 'He'll just be sorry I didn't manage to kill myself—that would have saved him the bother of going through a divorce.'

Those hazel eyes were completely unreadable. What was he thinking? She hadn't meant to tell him about her marital problems, but somehow it was a relief to talk about it.

'Why are you getting a divorce?' he enquired; there was a kind of empathy in the way he asked the question, and suddenly she was sure that he was divorced too.

'Why not?' She shrugged her shoulders, still trying to hide her hurt behind a pose of indifference. 'He wants to marry his secretary, and who am I to stand in the way of true love? Besides, she's pregnant.'

He looked surprised. 'Did you know he was having an affair?'

'Of course.' She was trying to make her voice sound cynical and hard, but she suspected it wasn't quite coming off. 'He has affairs with all his secretaries— it's just one of his endearing little habits.'

He laughed drily. 'So why didn't you leave him sooner?'

'I don't know,' she admitted with wry self-mockery. 'Habit, I suppose. And I didn't have anywhere else to go.'

'You don't have any family?'

'No—well, there's my father, of course, but I couldn't have gone there. I don't get on particularly well with my stepmother.'

'You could have got a place of your own.'

'Yes, I suppose so...' She looked down, swinging her foot in awkward embarrassment. How could she expect him to understand the way Colin had eroded so much of her confidence that she hadn't believed she could manage on her own? She wasn't at all sure that she could now—but at least she didn't have to think about it for a few more days. She wasn't well enough to leave Tom's yet, and go to a hotel.

There was a long silence. She could still feel his eyes resting on her, and a kind of shimmering heat had started deep inside her. Was he aware of the effect he had on her? She was fairly sure he must be—he was far too perceptive to miss the signs that gave her away.

She took another nervous sip of her coffee—by association, the taste had brought back with a thud the urgent craving for a cigarette, and it made her hands shake slightly, clattering the cup against the saucer. She hoped Tom wouldn't notice, but he did.

'What's wrong?' he asked quietly.

'I ... I've given up smoking.' Her smile was a brave effort, if a little brittle. 'It's nearly three hours since I had my last one.'

He laughed. 'Well done,' he approved. 'Keep it up.'

'I'll have to,' she responded, a slight edge of desperation in her voice. 'I've run out, and I don't think I could make it as far as the shops to buy a new packet.'

'And *I'm* certainly not going to go and buy them for you,' he confirmed with a quirk of sympathetic humour.

'I wouldn't ask you to.' She tilted her chin at a proud angle. 'I can manage.'

'Good for you.'

That devastating smile had unfurled itself unexpectedly, and her heartbeat skipped and began to race out of control. She could feel him looking at her, though she had bent her head to evade his eyes. A strange, electric tension seemed to fill the air between them. What was he thinking ...?

The sharp buzz of the telephone abruptly broke the spell. Tom went over to answer it, leaving her struggling to pull herself together. She wasn't actually listening to his conversation, but something caught her ear, making her pay sharper attention.

'All right, Vanessa—leave her in her stall, and keep her quiet, and I'll be over as soon as I can. Though, from what you say, it doesn't sound too serious.'

Vanessa—was that the elegant blonde who had called this afternoon? She had wasted little time in summoning him to her side. And after he had seen to her horse, what then? She was quite sure there was more to it than a simple professional call to a sick animal.

And there would be plenty of nice warm hay in a stable... An image rose in her mind, so vivid it almost took her breath away—of Tom and the elegant blonde tumbling in the hay, laughing, tugging at each other's clothes in passionate impatience...

A sharp stab of jealousy shot through her, and she shook her head, trying to dispel the tormenting vision. *Stupid*, she warned herself angrily. Don't let yourself be so vulnerable—at the very least don't let him see.

He put down the receiver, and glanced across at her. 'I have to go out,' he said, neither his voice nor his eyes giving anything away.

She forced some kind of smile. 'Oh. Fine. Well ... I'll see you later, then.'

'I doubt it,' he responded bluntly. 'I probably won't be back till quite late.'

'Oh.' So she had been right, then. 'Well, goodnight.'

'Goodnight.' And, picking up his car keys from the shelf above the fireplace, he was gone.

Josey woke to another beautiful sunny morning. She still felt a little stiff, but not nearly as bad as yesterday. It was strange how quickly one could adapt, she reflected, gazing around with pleasure at the cosy little room, tucked under the eaves of the cottage. London—and Colin—seemed light-years away. She felt as if she had lived here all her life.

She didn't know what time Tom had come in last night—she had taken a couple of her sleeping tablets. It was none of her business if Tom was having an affair with that woman, she had told herself firmly. And yet...she couldn't help thinking that he deserved something better. Oh, he could be cold and arrogant at times, but there was another side to him, that she had seen yesterday in his dedicated concern for the little black and white dog. He needed a woman who could bring that out in him...

Like you, for instance? she asked herself tartly. Don't be a fool—you couldn't compete with that elegant creature, not any more. Suddenly the urgent craving for a cigarette came rushing in on her, and she groaned, remembering that she didn't have any. How on earth was she going to get through the day without one?

The sunshine streaming in, and the blue sky she could glimpse through a chink in the curtains seemed to taunt her. How could she even think of polluting such a clean, fresh morning with choking cigarette smoke? Dragging herself out of bed, she wrapped herself up in an old tartan dressing-gown that Tom had lent her, and padded over to look out of the window.

Often, when she had been stuck in the middle of London, on some crowded street of hurrying, hassled people, with nothing around her but concrete buildings, and hard grey pavement beneath her feet, she had dreamed of one day living in the country. And this was what she had dreamed.

The house was built in an L-shape, with the single-storey wing that housed the veterinary clinic running back from the main part of the building. A low wall

enclosed a small, muddy concrete yard—and beyond
that the vast acres of fields ran on to the sky.

It was a land of clear distances; of broad, bright
sky and still water. Drawing a deep breath, she was
sure she could scent the salty tang of the distant Wash.
Somewhere a warbler was singing in the sedge, and
high in the sunlight a gull was calling with his coarse
kee-har.

A sudden quick movement on the low roof of the
clinic wing caught her eye. A small red squirrel was
running along the edge of the guttering, perfectly bal-
anced, his breakfast clutched tightly in his tiny hand.
As she watched, he paused at the end of the roof,
darting a swift glance around with his bright button
eyes, his ears alert for any sound of danger.

She hardly dared breathe in case he startled away,
and when she heard the door open behind her she
held up her hand, whispering, 'Shh.' Tom set her
breakfast tray down carefully on the chest beside the
bed, and came over to see what she was looking at.

The squirrel sat there for a few moments, its head
tipped quizzically on one side, and then, apparently
deciding that all was safe, it bent its head to tuck into
its morning meal, its sharp teeth making short work
of whatever it was.

Behind her, Tom chuckled softly. 'Ah, yes—he's
quite tame, that one. It's unusual for a red to come
so close—they're much shyer than the greys, but he
often comes right up to the house.'

He was very close to her, close enough so that she
could breathe that subtle male muskiness of his skin
that made her heart beat so erratically. With a struggle
she managed to maintain some sort of composure.

'Wh...what do they eat at this time of year?' she asked.

'Oh, reds live on hazelnuts and pine-cones,' he told her. 'They'll eat acorns, but for some reason we don't really understand yet they can't get the nutrition they need from them. They're not so adaptable as the greys, which is why they've been displaced almost everywhere else in the country. But here they seem to be holding on—the habitat seems to suit them.'

Josey nodded with interest, discreetly edging away from him. 'Oh...you've brought my breakfast up,' she murmured, glancing at the tray. 'Thank you, but...you needn't have bothered, really—I could have come downstairs.'

He slanted her a dry smile. 'You must be feeling better this morning,' he commented, an inflexion of sardonic humour in his voice. 'Yesterday you looked at me as if breakfast was a dirty word.'

'I'm sorry...' She caught herself up, laughing shyly, as she realised she was apologising yet again. 'I'm sorry, I won't keep saying that,' she promised, moving over to sit down on the edge of the bed. 'Oh, dear,' she sighed wryly, surveying the laden breakfast tray, 'Vi must really think I need feeding up!'

'You don't have to eat it all.'

'When I was small,' she said, smiling wistfully at the memory, 'if I left any food on my plate my mother always used to tell me there were starving children in poor countries who would love to have what I was wasting.'

'So you told her to wrap it up in a parcel and send it to them?' he suggested, sharing her amusement.

'Is that what you told your mother?' she asked, laughing.

He nodded, that glorious smile in full flight. 'It's probably a conversation that has taken place at every family meal-table at one time or another.'

Suddenly Josey found herself wondering what he had been like as a little boy. He must have been extremely intelligent, to have become a vet; she could imagine him always asking questions, and never being satisfied with fobbed-off answers. He must have been quite a handful...

His swift movement startled her, and too late she realised that he had snatched up her bottle of sleeping tablets from the chest beside the bed. 'What the hell are these?' he demanded.

'My... my tablets. Give them to me,' she pleaded, grabbing at them.

But he held them out of her reach as he read the label. 'Sleeping tablets? What do you need sleeping tablets for? How long have you been taking them?'

'Oh... about... three or four years...'

'Three or four *years*?'

'I was having trouble sleeping,' she explained, her voice unsteady.

He looked down at her, those deep hazel eyes unreadable. 'You really are a mess, aren't you?' he commented with dry humour.

Sharp tears were stinging the backs of her eyes; she very nearly hated him. 'Give them back to me,' she insisted rawly. 'You've no right to take them off me.'

He lifted one dark eyebrow, as if challenging her to contest him. 'You don't need them,' he asserted. 'You could sleep just as well without them. They've just become a habit.'

'I *do* need them,' she cried, almost desperate. 'I want them—give them to me.'

'No.' He tossed the bottle up and caught it, and put it in his pocket. 'I'll take charge of these. How many have you been taking a night?'

'T . . . two.'

'Well, tonight you can have one. Let's see how you get on with that for a few days, and then we'll cut it down to a half.'

'No!' She could feel herself beginning to panic. 'I'll never manage on a half. You don't understand—I can't sleep without them. I have tried, honestly, but it's awful.'

'It would be if I made you stop them all at once. But lowering the dose slowly will give your body time to adjust. I think you'll find you're sleeping perfectly well. And anyway,' he added with infuriating logic, 'what does it matter if you don't sleep? You don't have anything of earth-shattering importance to do— it won't hurt you to have less than the traditional eight hours.'

She sank back into a miserable huddle on the bed, her eyes glittering up at him in hostile defiance. 'Isn't it enough for you that I've given up smoking?' she complained bitterly.

He laughed with just the faintest trace of mockery. 'But that was rather *force majeure* than will-power, wasn't it?' he taunted. 'You couldn't make it as far as the shops to buy yourself a new packet.'

'So?' she retorted. 'I've given them up—isn't that all that matters?'

'I suppose it is,' he conceded with dry humour. 'Maybe that car accident will turn out to have been a blessing in disguise after all, if it gives you the chance to get your head straightened out. Now eat your breakfast. I've got to go out—I'll see you later.'

He went out, closing the door behind him—her tablets still safely in his pocket. She eyed the breakfast tray with a baleful glare. She would have liked to have been able to ignore it, as some sort of gesture of defiance, but she was too hungry. It must be all the fresh country air, she reflected as she tucked in—something had certainly sharpened her appetite.

And it was hard to maintain her simmering resentment at Tom for the high-handed way he had acted, when every thought of that rare, beautiful smile could make her bones melt. Of course it was stupid— hadn't she had enough of arrogant, domineering men?

But Tom was totally different from Colin. Colin had coerced and manipulated her entirely for his own benefit, so that everything in their lives would be just as he wanted it. Tom was doing it for her own good. It was just that she felt like some pathetic little waif he had rescued—and she didn't want him to see her like that. She didn't want him to see her like that at all.

Tom had been ruthless about only allowing her one sleeping pill, but, though it was the last thing she would have admitted to him, Josey found that he had been right. True, she didn't sleep particularly well, surfacing to wakefulness several times during the night, but she didn't feel nearly so heavy-headed in the morning.

The effects of the accident were beginning to wear off too. She had some fine bruises all down the right side of her body, and her wrist was still painful, but the stiffness had gone. And she was finding that she could survive without a cigarette, though the craving still lingered.

Tom hadn't brought her breakfast—he had warned her that he had to go out early, to visit several local farms for routine testing of their cows for the Ministry of Agriculture. Instead she had eaten breakfast downstairs in the cosy kitchen, chatting to Vi.

She would have had no chance of clearing up the daunting pile on her plate without a little discreet help from Jethro, who padded quietly to her side as soon as Vi went back into the scullery to fetch the tea-pot, and disposed of her bacon and eggs as neatly as a pickpocket, swallowing it so swiftly that it couldn't have touched the sides.

'There, that's what I like to see!' approved Vi as she waddled back into the kitchen and saw the empty plate. 'We'll get a bit of meat on you yet.'

The door from the surgery opened, and a young girl in a green nylon tabard-overall appeared. She glanced around the kitchen, and her brown eyes focused on Josey in unmistakable hostility. Josey hid a smile of wry humour— Oh, no, not *another* one, she mused to herself.

At a second glance, she decided that the girl wasn't quite as young as she had first thought—perhaps in her early twenties. But her long, thick mane of brown hair was far too over-powering for her small face, giving her the appearance of a nervous little mouse peering out from a thicket. She could have been quite pretty if she would only have it cut, Josey decided fairly.

'Isn't Tom here?' the girl asked, turning to Vi.

'You know he's not,' came the slightly impatient reply. 'It's Ministry day.'

'Oh...' The girl had a vacuous sort of voice, and it was more than clear that Vi had little time for her. 'Where's the mop and bucket?'

'In the scullery, where it's always been.'

The girl nodded, and with another malevolent glance in Josey's direction she went across to fetch what she had come for, and vanished back into the surgery.

'Silly little flibbertigibbet,' Vi sniffed in scorn. 'Always mooning around, getting on poor Tom's nerves.'

'Who is she?' enquired Josey.

'Sandra—Tom's assistant in the surgery. Trouble is, she fancies herself in love with him. He wouldn't keep her on, but it's not easy to get a trained veterinary assistant out here in the middle of nowhere.'

'Oh...' Josey nodded. 'Here, let me help with that,' she added quickly as Vi began to clear the table.

'Oh, no, you don't,' she scolded. 'That wrist o'yourn ain't up to using properly yet a while. You wait till the doctor says it's all right.'

'But I hate sitting around with nothing to do,' Josey protested. 'Maybe I could just cut some flowers, and bring them into the house? Those roses at the front smell so lovely.'

Vi's broad smile beamed out. 'Ay—that'd be nice,' she agreed. 'There's been nothing like that since *she* left.'

The epithet was uttered darkly, and Josey's curiosity leapt. Casually she turned to the kitchen drawer to search for a pair of scissors. 'Do you mean Tom's wife?' she enquired, hoping the tone of her voice was not giving away the depth of her interest.

'Ay—her.' Vi's contempt of the ex Mrs Quinn was undisguised. 'Flighty piece, she was—never was content with living down here. Always on at him to take her back to London.'

'Oh? She came from London, then?' Josey probed cautiously.

Vi nodded grimly. 'Met her when he was up at the university. Some kind of model, she was—all very glamorous, I suppose, but not the right sort for him to marry. He was going to come straight back here as soon as he'd qualified, and be partners with his uncle, but she talked him into staying on down there.'

Vi was getting into her stride, and Josey simply nodded, not wanting to interrupt the flow of gossip.

'Well, it was never going to work out—anyone could see he'd be miserable, stuck down there in the big city. It weren't what he was cut out for. Not that she could say he didn't give it a fair chance—four years he stuck it, afore he came back.'

'He . . . left her, then?' she enquired, helpless in the grip of an insatiable curiosity.

Vi shook her head. 'Oh, no—she came back with him. But she didn't stay very long—inside of three months she was complaining she was bored. Nagging him all the time, she was—terrible rows. Then she met some fancy architect chap, down here doing up the old windmill over by Saltham Marsh, and next thing she'd packed her bags and gone off with him.'

So I was right, Josey mused with grim satisfaction. Tom *was* divorced. And maybe what Vi had told her explained a little of his cynical attitude towards her that first evening—he must have had his fill of London girls.

But what a silly woman his wife had been, she reflected almost incredulously. How could anyone prefer the hard grey city streets to this green paradise? And how could any woman walk away from a man like Tom Quinn?

CHAPTER FOUR

AFTER Vi had gone, Josey's main problem was boredom. She went through to the surgery to see how Shep was getting on, but Sandra was there, and made it very clear that this was her domain, and that she resented intruders. Josey retreated back to the cottage, and tried to entertain herself for the rest of the day with the magazines or the television.

It was late afternoon by the time Tom arrived home. Jethro jumped up, pawing at the door, before Josey even heard a sound. There had been quite a few cars pass during the day, but Jethro had ignored all of them—just one sent him into a fever of anticipation.

Tom looked tired. He was carrying two large cool-boxes, and had trouble getting through the door, so keen was Jethro to welcome him. 'Down,' he commanded crisply, and the collie immediately crouched to the floor, all alert obedience.

Josey had risen to her feet. 'Can I take one of those for you?' she offered, coming forward.

He shook his head. 'No, it's all right—I've just got to put them in the fridge in the clinic.'

'I'll open the doors for you, then . . .'

'I said it's all right!'

His tone was abrupt, and she felt her own anger rise in response. 'OK—there's no need to bite my head off,' she protested, startled by the sharpness in her own voice. 'A simple, "no, thank you," would do.'

He looked taken aback, but then conceded a wry smile. 'I'm sorry, Brucellosis testing isn't exactly my favourite pastime, but it has to be done. Maybe you could make me a cup of coffee?'

When he smiled like that, she could forgive him anything. 'Of...of course.' She retreated quickly to the scullery before he should notice that her cheeks had tinged a deep shade of pink.

She had no trouble making the coffee this time, and carried it through to the office. Tom was at his desk, his head bent over a pile of accounts, and he barely even glanced up as she came in. 'Thanks—just put it down...wherever you can find space.' He waved a hand in a vague gesture around the small room.

Josey glanced around, a glint of sardonic humour in her eyes. The place was a mess. Every available surface—chairs, table-tops, the windowsill, even the floor—was cluttered with jumbles of paperwork. It was clear that office organisation was not his strong point! 'Is there anything I can do to help?' she asked, diffident at offering after the brusque way he had brushed aside even her offer to open a door for him.

He looked up at her, his expression guarded. 'Are you any good at filing?' he asked reluctantly.

'Of course I am! I was a secretary for eight years, you know.'

'Well, the stuff's supposed to go in that filing-cabinet,' he conceded, almost grudging. 'If you fancy tidying some of it up for me, you're more than welcome.'

She nodded, accepting the challenge. And the paperwork really was in a mess—invoices for drugs were all muddled up with duplicates of returns to the Ministry of Agriculture, mail-shots from pharmaceutical companies and back issues of the *Veterinary Record*.

'Some of this stuff is months old!' she protested. 'Why don't you employ someone to deal with it for you, if you don't have time yourself?'

He slanted her a sardonic look. 'How much money do you think a practice like this makes?' he enquired.

'Well . . . couldn't Sandra do some of it?'

'She has enough to do with her own job. Besides,' he added, his tone hinting at past scenes that had severely strained his patience, 'I don't want her in here, meddling with everything and making a damned nuisance of herself.'

Josey concealed a wry smile. He couldn't have made it any plainer that he didn't welcome unsubtle displays of female adoration. She could take that as a warning. 'Aren't you afraid that I'll make a nuisance of myself?' she challenged, trying for a light tone.

He slanted her a look that contained just a hint of appreciative amusement. 'But you were a secretary,' he rejoined smartly. 'For eight years!'

Josey was surprised. He hadn't shown much sign of possessing a sense of humour before—it added a whole new dimension to him. If only he weren't so cool and stand-offish all the time—he could really be quite charming.

But then maybe it was understandable that he was so wary of women, she reflected fairly. There must be so many trying to pursue him; Vanessa, and Sandra, even that pretty young nurse at the hospital—and those were only the ones she knew about. And after his one disastrous experience of marriage he had every reason to be cynical.

He must have been quite young when he had met his wife, if he had still been at university, she mused, thinking back over what Vi had told her. And he must have loved her a great deal, if he had been prepared to endure four years of living in the city, when he hated it so much, just for her sake.

She smiled in secret amusement at the back of that tousled dark head, bent over his desk like that of a reluctant schoolboy who would far rather be out in the open air. She really couldn't imagine him being polite to all those rich old beldames with their pampered pooches—it must have strained his patience to the limit.

It was pleasant, working alongside him, though they didn't speak much except for the few occasions when she needed to check something with him. She soon found a technique for managing the papers with her good hand, slipping the injured one out of its sling to hold things down.

To her amusement, she found that Tom had a habit of grunting impatiently to himself as he worked over his accounts—it was clearly the part of his job that he relished least. Glancing over his shoulder, she found that most of it was really rather routine stuff.

'Why don't you show me how to do that, and I'll finish it for you tomorrow?' she suggested.

He glanced up at her in sceptical enquiry. 'Why would you want to be bothered with this?'

His reluctance to allow her to take over a task that he found onerous was puzzling—unless it was that his self-sufficiency was so precious to him that he was afraid to give up even the smallest ounce of it. 'Because I'd like to make myself useful. You've been very kind to me, and I'd like to repay you in some way.

And besides,' she added, seeing that he was still looking doubtful, 'I'm getting bored, sitting around with nothing to do. Please?'

'OK,' he conceded, happier with the idea that he was doing her a favour than that she was doing him one. 'Pull that chair over, and I'll show you what to do.'

It was simple enough, for anyone who had had the sort of grounding she had had in office administration. Within ten minutes she felt confident that she had a reasonably good grasp of what to do. 'That's fine,' she said, nodding. 'I'll do them tomorrow, and then I'll finish off this filing.'

'Good. Thank you.' He managed that last with a little difficulty, as if he said it as rarely as he said sorry. A car had drawn up outside, and he glanced at his watch. 'That'll be Hugh. There's just time for another cup of coffee before we start the small-animal clinic.'

'I'll make it,' she offered at once, and hurried away to the kitchen.

The big old school-clock on the wall told her that it was gone five o'clock. Tom had left the house before eight o'clock this morning, and it was likely that it would be at least a couple of hours before he had finished in the clinic. He must be very dedicated to his work, she mused with a deep respect; he seemed to have very little free time.

Colin had been like that—always working, always fixing deals. Even their occasional holidays had been combined with business trips. But it had been so very different. What could you see for anything Colin had done? Pieces of paper, faxes, figures with endless rows of noughts behind them. Not a life saved, a small black and white dog with a thick dressing-pad on his tummy, sleeping peacefully, snuffling as he dreamed.

She put the mugs of coffee on a tray, and carried it through to the clinic. Tom was in the recovery-room, with a tall, grey-haired man who bore him such a striking resemblance that Josey would have guessed anywhere that they were related. The two of them were examining Shep's stitches.

'A very neat job, my boy,' the older man approved, as if his nephew were still a young student, wet behind the ears. 'Well done.' He turned as Josey came into the room. 'Ah coffee! Excellent!'

'Josey, this is my uncle Hugh,' Tom introduced her with casual informality. 'Hugh—Josey Rutherford.'

'Ah, yes!' He twinkled her a smile. 'How do you do, Mrs Rutherford? I'm very pleased to meet you. And how's your wrist? Tom's been telling me you were in a car accident.'

'Oh, it's quite a bit better now, thank you.' She smiled back at him, liking him instantly. He had an air of calm stillness about him, which she guessed would be very reassuring to a sick, frightened animal. And, though he must have been curious about her relationship with his nephew, he didn't show it. 'But please, call me Josey,' she added warmly.

'Josey.' He nodded. 'What a very pretty name. It suits you.' He took his coffee, stirring in two spoonfuls of sugar. 'So you're old Florrie Calder's niece,' he remarked musingly. 'And now that old cottage of hers is yours, of course. Have you been out to look at it yet?'

'No. But I understand it's not in a very good state of repair.' She slanted a swift glance towards Tom, but his face was totally inscrutable. 'Did you know my aunt well?' she added, turning back to the older man.

'Old Florrie? Indeed I did. She always had a bit of a menagerie up at that old place—stray dogs and cats that no one else wanted.' He smiled reminiscently. 'I often used to drop by, even when there was no call. To be honest, it was her blackberry and apple pie that was the lure—I've never tasted anything like it!'

'Oh, yes!' The memories came back to Josey, of sitting in her aunt's pretty cottage, eating great wedges of pie with fresh local cream. 'Her pastry used to melt in your mouth.'

'And her Eccles cakes! I don't know what she used to put in them, but they were the best Eccles cakes that I've ever tasted.'

Josey laughed, trying to remember back down the years whether she had ever met this kindly gentleman when she had been a child, visiting her aunt. But it was a very long time since she had last been here, and the stays had only ever been short and infrequent. But even so, it felt like a link, as if in some small way she actually belonged here—the only place in the world she felt any part of her belonged.

There was a diffident tap on the door, and Sandra's head appeared. 'Oh. I'm...sorry to interrupt.' Her eyes were liquid adoration as they rested on Tom, though a second before they had flashed a hostile glare when they saw Josey standing there sipping coffee with the two men, apparently so very much at home. 'Shall I...Shall I start getting the surgery ready?'

'Of course,' Tom responded, a faint edge of impatience in his voice. 'And there was a drugs delivery this morning. Why haven't you put it away?'

The poor girl gazed up at him like a whipped puppy. 'I'm sorry—I thought you might want to look at them first.'

'It's just routine stuff—you should be capable of checking it off against the order yourself.'

'Yes, Tom,' she mumbled humbly, and retreated, closing the door.

He sat down with his coffee, catching Josey's eye in surprise as she slanted him a look of censure. 'What's wrong?' he asked.

'Do you always speak to people like that?' she challenged, braver on the young girl's behalf than she would ever have been on her own. 'Anyone would think she was some kind of skivvy.'

He looked taken aback, as if he genuinely hadn't realised how abrupt he had sounded. 'It's just that she can be so irritating at times, mooning around instead of getting on with her job,' he tried to explain.

'Even so, that's no excuse not to say "please" and "thank you" occasionally,' she reminded him with a touch of asperity.

Quite suddenly that incredible smile unfurled itself. 'I'm sorry,' he conceded. 'I'll try to watch my manners in future.'

The mock humility in his voice made her eyes dance with amusement, and Hugh sat watching them in quiet satisfaction. 'Well, I suppose we'd better go and see what the world is going to bring to our door this evening,' he remarked, rising to his feet. 'Very nice to have met you, Josey. I'll see you again later.'

Now that she was recovering from the effects of her accident, Josey knew that she really ought to be thinking of moving out. The whole village must know that she was here, ''living'' with Tom—and they would all be making wildly inaccurate assumptions about what was going on. If she was going to settle here, and be accepted, she really needed to move into her own cottage as quickly as possible.

It was Tom's weekend on call, and an emergency on one of the farms kept him out for most of Saturday, but Sunday seemed quiet, so after lunch she decided to take the bull by the horns. 'I was just wondering . . .'

He glanced up from his perusal of the Sunday newspaper; he was sitting in one of the deep, comfortable armchairs, his long legs stretched out in front of him, Jethro asleep with his head draped over his feet in blissful devotion. For one wild moment, she could visualise herself spending every Sunday afternoon like this . . .

'If you have time this afternoon, do you think you could take me up to have a look at the cottage?' she blurted out.

The dark look he shot her took her by surprise.

'Of course, if you're too busy, or too tired . . .' she stammered hastily.

'Oh, no.' His hazel eyes stared back at her in hard disdain. 'Maybe you ought to have a look at it—then you might think twice about this daft notion you have of living in it.'

She regarded him in wary uncertainty. At least it sounded like a 'yes'—but why should he be so annoyed? What did it matter to him if she chose to live there? 'Thank you,' she murmured, deciding that it was best not to argue about it at the moment. 'I'll . . . get my jacket.'

Josey had all but forgotten what the cottage looked like—she had only the vaguest recollection of it, tucked away from the road down a narrow, winding lane, overhung by trees. But when they came to it, she could hardly even see it—in the dark, she would have driven right past.

It was much smaller than she remembered. The high hawthorn hedge that had surrounded the neat little garden was wild and overgrown, almost merging with the trees around it—their branches hung right over the slate-tiled roof, only the old-fashioned chimney-pots jutting up from the shadows.

Tom parked the Land Rover, and she got out, Jethro running at her heels. The wooden gate had fallen off its hinges, and the garden path was so overgrown that she couldn't even find it. Stepping carefully, she picked her way through the tangle of weeds to the front door.

Tom followed her up the path, his expression grim, his hands deep in the pockets of his well-worn cord jeans. She tried to ignore the disparaging glance he cast at the window-frames and the roof—it just needed a little attention, that was all.

'I've got the key somewhere—the solicitor who dealt with the deeds sent it, and I just put it on my key-ring. Why do key-rings always fall to the very bottom of your handbag?' she added, laughing nervously. She knew that she was babbling like a fool, but his silence was making her tense. He really was the most moody, difficult man she had ever met—worse even than Colin, and that was saying something!

She found her keys at last, and pushed open the door, stepping inside with a certain amount of trepidation. It wasn't as bad as she had anticipated. It was cold, in spite of the warmth of the summer afternoon, and there was a rather musty smell, but a good airing would soon dispel that.

Everything was exactly as her aunt had left it—the dark Victorian paintings on the walls, the fussy little ornaments cluttering the fireplace and the old-fashioned walnut sideboard that had always gleamed with beeswax and elbow-grease, now dulled by a thick coating of dust.

As she looked around, she felt a stab of guilt. She should have visited more, should have come sooner to sort everything out after her aunt had died. It had been the old lady's home for over seventy years, and now it looked so forlorn and neglected. But already she could visualise how she wanted it to look, with light cane furniture, and bowls of flowers everywhere.

'Well,' she mused with growing enthusiasm, 'this could be made really quite cosy.'

Tom merely grunted, so she ignored him, impatient with his obstinate disapproval. Crossing to the door beside the fireplace, she found herself in a dark, cramped lobby. To her left were the two small bed-rooms—there was no bathroom, and the lavatory, she recalled with a twist of wry humour, was in a freezing cold privy at the end of the garden path.

Beyond the lobby was the kitchen, and as she pushed open the door she groaned in horror. It was going to take more than just a little redecoration to deal with this! In the corner of the ceiling was a great gaping hole, open through the roof. Rain had poured in, building up black mould on the walls, and the quarry-tiled floor was a mess. It was going to be a major job to make it habitable again—and it was going to be expensive.

That was something she hadn't really thought about when she had left Colin. It had never really occurred to her to wonder how she would earn her living—for so many years she had had the allowance that he had paid her. Of course, there were the investments that he had put into her name, for tax purposes, but those weren't really hers.

Perhaps it was just an empty dream, after all, to think that she could actually live out here in the country. The only career she had any experience of, apart from being a society wife, was as a secretary— and there probably wasn't very much call for secretaries around here.

Tom had followed her into the kitchen, and was standing looking around, his hands thrust deep into the pockets of his old cord jeans. 'Well, this is a bit of a mess,' he remarked drily.

'Yes, it is,' she countered, her voice sharp. 'You don't have to say "I told you so".'

'Did I say that?' he taunted, his tone implying that it was precisely what he had been thinking.

'No,' she conceded. 'But you don't seem at all keen on the idea of my living here.'

He shrugged his wide shoulders in a gesture of supreme indifference. 'I don't give a damn where you live,' he asserted coldly. 'What I do object to is yet another holiday cottage in the area. We have quite enough already. The villages are dying because local families can't afford to get on the housing ladder, and they're forced to move away, taking the future with them.'

'But I don't intend it to be a holiday-cottage,' she asserted, quietly firm. 'I'm going to live here—it's going to be my home.'

He laughed with biting scorn. 'Live here? You won't live here,' he sneered. 'Oh, yes, it all looks very pretty now, in the summer, with the sky blue and everything green. But what about when the winter comes? Have you any idea what winter's like out here in the fens? When the mists come up off the waters, and creep into everything, like ice, and the roads are flooded so you can't get into town, and the pipes are frozen and the electricity's down?'

'Well, how did my aunt manage?'

'You're not your aunt.' He might have been trying to pretend at the beginning that he didn't care either way, but now there was no mistaking the aggressive bite in his voice. 'She grew up here—she knew the hardships, she knew how to survive. You don't belong.'

'Oh, I see.' Her voice was very cold, very controlled. 'I'm an outsider, and you don't want me here. Is that what you told your wife? Is that why she left you?'

His eyes flared, and he grabbed her roughly by the shoulders. 'Who told you about Julia?' he demanded fiercely.

'Does it matter?' she countered, returning his gaze with cool defiance, refusing to let him see that inside she was trembling at his sudden anger. 'When I first heard about her, I felt sorry for you—I thought she must have been a bitch. But now I'm not so sure.'

'Don't feel sorry for me,' he grated. 'I was well rid of her.'

'Oh, I'm sure you were. You probably like it much better, living on your own. You really don't like women, do you?'

His eyes had darkened quite frighteningly. 'Oh, yes, I like women,' he returned, his voice menacingly soft. 'But only for one thing.'

His fingers were gripping her shoulders like a vice, and in one step he backed her against the old-fashioned stone sink, so that she couldn't escape. As she tried to turn her head away he caught her chin, lifting her face to his, and his mouth descended on hers, hard and insistent, crushing her lips apart. She tried to struggle free, but she was trapped, helpless against his superior strength, and his plundering tongue swept deep into her mouth in an invasion so forceful that she could not resist.

And suddenly she didn't want to resist. Her blood was swirling in her veins, dizzying her, and she lifted her arms to wrap them tightly around his neck, kissing him back. A fierce heat had ignited inside her, that she had never known before. Her body was crushed against his, every inch so intimately close that she could sense the potent warning of male arousal in him, and knew that he must be able to read every betraying signal of her own helpless response.

He lifted his head, dragging in a harsh breath, and she gazed up at him, bewildered by the impact of those few brief seconds. It was as if she had never been kissed before. There was a hint of question in his eyes—but before he could say anything there was a call from outside, a voice that Josey recognised at once.

'Hello? Is there anyone in there?'

The expression that crossed Tom's face was impossible to read, and he drew back quickly as intrusive footsteps crossed the outer room. Josey felt her cheeks flaming a heated scarlet, and it took a considerable effort of will to face the woman who appeared in the doorway.

They had met before. Those ice-blue eyes took in the scene in one glance, and there was no way she wouldn't have guessed what had been happening. 'Oh . . . I'm sorry. Am I interrupting something?' she purred, her voice dripping acid. 'I was out riding, and I saw your car in the lane, Tom. I was trying to ring you all day yesterday, but all I kept getting was that stupid answering service of yours.'

'What did you want, Vanessa?' he enquired. His voice was level, but Josey could sense the tension in his body, still close to hers.

The blonde twirled her riding whip in her hand, as if she would have liked to have used it on somebody. 'Oh, I just wanted to make sure you were coming to my party next weekend.' She turned to Josey with a saccharine smile. 'We call it a midsummer ball, but it's really terribly informal, just a few friends. You will come too, won't you?'

The last words were bitten out, and Josey eyed her with covert curiosity. Why on earth should Vanessa invite her to a party, when it was clear that the last thing she wanted was to have her around? Perhaps she hoped that it would be an opportunity to impress Tom with her superior beauty and elegance, she mused tartly.

A hitherto unsuspected spirit of rivalry woke inside her; maybe she couldn't quite compete as an equal, but she'd give this condescending madam a darned good run for her money! She returned the smile as insincerely as it had been given. 'How nice,' she purred, her fingers curling like a cat's claws, half unsheathed. 'I'd love to come.'

Tom slanted her a questioning glance, his mouth thinned. 'Thank you, Vanessa,' he grated, the words almost dragged out of him. 'We'll look forward to it—won't we, Josey?'

'Good.' The battle lines were drawn, and all that remained was for the formal declaration of war. 'Until Saturday, then.' With a fierce snap of her riding whip, Vanessa turned on the heel of her highly polished leather boot, and walked away.

Josey let go her breath with careful control, and moved discreetly away from Tom. If only she could guess what was going on in his mind as easily as he seemed able to guess what was going on in hers! She would have given almost anything to know the true nature of his relationship with the haughty blonde.

He slanted her the briefest look, his hands thrust deep into his pockets again. 'Well?' he demanded tersely. 'Have you seen enough of the cottage yet?'

She tilted her head at a proud angle. If he was going to behave as if that searing kiss had never happened, so could she! 'Yes, thank you,' she returned, and walking stiffly past him, she led the way back out to the Land Rover.

CHAPTER FIVE

IT WAS another slumbrous summer afternoon. Josey lay curled up on the big settee, with the two dogs snuggled up to her—Shep was now almost completely recovered, and had been allowed to come into the cottage, where Tom said he would recuperate better.

She was browsing idly through one of the battered old magazines Vi had found in the waiting-room; she had another thick wedge of Vi's moist, dark fruitcake to have with her cup of tea, and a heavy old bumble-bee was lumbering around the perfumed roses outside the window. As far as she was concerned, life could go on like this for ever.

But realistically she knew that it couldn't. Sooner or later she was going to have to start making a move to get her existence back into some kind of order; she couldn't stay here in Tom's cottage much longer. Her emotions were getting dangerously out of control, and after what had happened yesterday...

But what *had* happened? After he had kissed her, he had been as distant as if he were living on another planet. They had barely spoken as they had driven back to the house, and they had only just finished dinner when a telephone call had summoned him out to attend to a mare in foal.

Maybe she was making too much of it. After all, it hadn't exactly been a romantic kiss. It had been more like a punishment, for making him lose his temper by talking about his wife. That must still be quite a sore subject with him, she mused. Was he still in love with her?

Besides, he had warned her that it wouldn't be very easy to find a hotel room at this time of year, and until she had seen a solicitor she didn't know if she had any money or not. And any damage to her reputation had already been done—it couldn't make matters any worse if she stayed a few more days.

The click of the front gate brought the dogs' heads up, but they didn't growl. Vanessa again? wondered Josey. But why should she call? She must know that Tom would be out at this time of the afternoon. But the voice that called a friendly 'Hello?' certainly wasn't Vanessa's.

'Come in,' she responded, swinging her feet off the settee; she didn't need to go and answer the door—it was never locked.

A dark-haired young woman, about the same age as herself, appeared on the threshold. 'Hi,' she greeted Josey with easy warmth. 'Can I come in? I'm Helen—Tom's sister-in-law.'

'Yes, of course,' Josey responded at once. 'He isn't in at the moment, though—he's gone out on his calls.'

'Oh, that's OK—I dropped in to see you. I brought you these.' She put a bag of books and magazines down on the table. 'I thought you might like a bit of company for a change.'

'Yes, I would!' Josey confirmed sincerely. 'Would you like some tea?'

'I'd love some. And is that some of Vi's home-made cake I see? I know I shouldn't, but I can resist anything except temptation!'

Josey laughed. 'I'll cut you a thin slice,' she offered.

'A *very* thin slice,' pleaded Helen, wryly patting her hips. 'I adore my children, but I'm afraid the process of having them has given me a real farmer's wife's figure.'

'And I'm trying to put a bit of weight on,' Josey confessed. 'Isn't it funny how we women are never satisfied with the figures we've got?'

'It's all these goddesses in the magazines,' remarked Helen, gesturing towards the old copy of *Cosmopolitan* Josey had been reading. 'They're intimidating.'

'Mmm,' agreed Josey, bringing the tea over to the table. 'I like her hair, though. I wonder if mine would suit me like that? I was thinking of getting it cut.'

Helen regarded the picture critically. 'Yes, I think it would. There's quite a decent hairdressers in town, you know. You could ring up for an appointment.'

'Is there a dress shop too?' asked Josey, her smile a little crooked. 'I...I need something for Saturday—something suitable for a party. I haven't really got anything I could wear.'

'Ah, Vanessa's!' chuckled Helen. 'Yes, you must have something special to wear for that!'

Josey looked at her in surprise. 'But she said it was going to be informal,' she protested.

Helen shook her head firmly. 'Don't you believe it. *She'll* be dolled up to the nines, just to show the rest of us country bumpkins what style is all about. I'd love to see you put her nose out of joint.'

'Oh, I don't know about that,' demurred Josey with a blush of modesty. 'She's...very attractive.'

'Oh, yes,' agreed Helen, a twist of wry humour in her voice. 'She's beautiful, all right. You'd never believe she's my cousin, would you? I think the family genes were shared out most unfairly!'

'Your cousin? Oh...' Josey hesitated, embarrassed, but Helen gurgled with laughter.

'Oh, don't worry,' she assured her quickly. 'Just because she's my cousin, I don't have to like her. Though, to be fair,' she added musingly, 'she used to be nice enough, when she was a kid. But now she's Lady Fordham-Jones she's a royal pain in the butt!'

'*Lady* Fordham-Jones?' Josey's eyes danced with humour, though her mind was working swiftly. She should have guessed that Vanessa was married—that explained the ambivalence in Tom's attitude towards her. However much he was attracted, he would be reluctant to have an affair—particularly after what had happened to his own marriage. 'I didn't realise I'd been honoured with an invitation from a member of the aristocracy,' she skitted lightly.

'Very minor aristocracy,' Helen assured her. 'Gerald's just a baronet. Bit of a chinless wonder, of course, but if you want a title and a big country house stuffed full of antiques you can't have everything! Though, mind you,' she confided candidly, 'I've always thought there was more to it than that.'

'Oh?' Josey was learning very quickly that gossip was the major pastime around here.

'I probably shouldn't be telling you this,' Helen demurred a little hesitantly. 'But you're bound to hear it anyway. I think it was because Tom had married Julia. Everyone had always assumed that he and Vanessa would get it together once he'd finished university, and it was her way of saving face.'

'Oh.' Suddenly everything was falling into place. Josey could almost feel sorry for the haughty blonde—

the disappointment she must have suffered must have been very hard to bear. 'I've ... heard about Julia,' she remarked diffidently. 'I gather she didn't stay here very long.'

Helen snorted. 'She didn't stay five minutes! I thought from the first time I saw her that Tom was an idiot to marry her, but there you go. Of course, she was absolutely gorgeous-looking, and men just don't think with their brains when they're young—they think with the other thing!'

Josey laughed, nodding a wry agreement. And it wasn't only young men who were prone to allow the power of a purely physical attraction to undermine their common sense, she admitted privately. Women of thirty-one could do it too. 'It was a shame for Vanessa,' she commented aloud. 'I mean, how ironic—with Tom's marriage not lasting very long, if she'd only waited ...'

'That's true,' agreed Helen, her head tipped on one side. 'Mind you, she's not given up hope—she's always after him, every chance she gets. But you don't have to worry,' she added seriously. 'She's wasting her time. The last thing Tom would do is have an affair with a married woman—besides, Gerald happens to be a very good friend of his.'

Josey felt her cheeks tinge with pink. So even Tom's sister-in-law was leaping to conclusions. 'Look, I ... Maybe I ought to set the record straight,' she managed with difficulty. 'I'm ... not having an affair with him, either. We only met a few days ago—I smashed up my car...'

'Yes, I know—and broke your wrist.' Helen smiled. 'He told me.'

'He seems to make quite a habit of rescuing lame ducks,' Josey remarked, trying to smile. 'He was telling me that when he was young he was always bringing injured birds and rabbits down here when it was his uncle's practice.'

Helen laughed. 'Yes, he was—but I'm not quite sure I'd put you in that category,' she added, clearly not convinced by Josey's protestations. 'Anyway, listen,' she went on, to Josey's relief changing the subject. 'I want to buy a new dress for Vanessa's do, too. Why don't we go into town together? Now that my youngest is in school, I can enjoy a bit of freedom. What about Wednesday? Will you feel up to it?'

'Yes, of course—and I'd like that,' Josey agreed readily. 'Thank you.'

'There's Norwich—look, you can see the spire of the Cathedral.'

Josey peered out through the windscreen. Indeed she could see the spire, rising gracefully above the city, glistening white in the sun. 'Isn't it beautiful?' she breathed. 'And you can see it for miles.'

'It's the second highest spire in England,' Helen informed her proudly. 'And, of course, it's built on the higher ground.'

'I always thought Norfolk would be flat and boring,' mused Josey. 'But it isn't—boring, I mean. And just look at that sky. I never took much notice of it before—I suppose you can't really see so much of it in London, so you're not so aware of it. But here, the clouds are always different—I never get tired of watching them.'

Helen slanted her a glance of understanding. 'Me, too—and I've lived here all my life.' She twisted her wrist to glance at her watch. 'Eleven o'clock, did you say was your appointment with Oliver? We'll be there in plenty of time.'

Josey smiled wryly. 'I'm glad you came with me,' she confided. 'I feel as if I'm going to the dentist.'

Helen laughed. 'Don't be silly,' she encouraged. 'Olly's really nice—he was at school with my Donald. And once you've sorted everything out we can get down to some serious shopping!'

They parked the car close to the town centre, and walked to the solicitor's office. Josey found herself wishing desperately that she had a cigarette, but fortunately she didn't have to wait in the fusty little waiting-room for more than a few moments. Mr Riley, a dapper little man in a grey suit, appeared almost at once.

'Mrs Rutherford? Will you come in now, please? Oh, Helen—hello,' he added warmly, recognising who was with her. 'How are you? And how's the family?'

'We're all fine, thank you.'

That brief social exchange helped Josey relax a little, and once in his office she found that his calm, businesslike approach made it much easier than she had feared it would be to explain all the painful details of her failed marriage.

When she had finished he leaned back in his chair and took off his glasses, placing them down carefully on his desk beside the pages of notes he had taken. 'Well, Mrs Rutherford,' he commented with easy confidence, 'I certainly think you will have an excellent case to claim a quite substantial settlement. As you say, you helped your husband to establish his company, and he made you a co-director. And of course the property and shares he has already put into your name he can't touch.'

'But he only put them in my name for tax purposes,' she reminded him.

He shook his head. 'No matter why he did it, those are yours. I'll prepare an affidavit, and we'll file at once on the grounds of his adultery.'

'Thank you.' She managed a smile. 'I'll be glad to get it all over with.'

'Of course. And I dare say he will be too, with a new baby on the way.' His eyes glinted with a belligerent light. 'I don't expect he'll want to quibble for too long over the financial details.'

'No...' She felt a twinge of guilt at using that to almost blackmail Colin into agreeing to her demands—but, after all, he had brought it on himself. 'And—er—what about my charge cards, Mr Riley? I really need to use them for a little longer—I'll have to buy some clothes, and one or two other things.'

He shrugged his shoulders in an expansive gesture. 'You can use them as much as you like,' he assured her. 'It's up to your husband to cancel them.'

'I see.' She drew a long, steadying breath, and rose to her feet. 'Well, thank you very much, Mr Riley.'

'Thank *you*, Mrs Rutherford.' He rose too, and offered her his hand in farewell. 'I'll contact you as soon as I hear from your husband's solicitors.'

'Yes.' She nodded, with another flickering smile, and, rather grateful that the ordeal was over, she hurried out to the waiting-room, where Helen was sitting reading a magazine.

'All done?' she enquired cheerfully.

'For now. I could do with a coffee.'

'Right. And then—to the shops!'

Josey laughed. 'Well . . . at least I can still use my charge cards.'

Helen's eyes danced with mischief. 'Good. So you can be really extravagant.'

'Well . . .'

'Of course you can,' her friend insisted stoutly. 'After what he did to you? Take him to the cleaners!'

The absence of the Land Rover told Josey that Tom wasn't in when they got back—she was rather glad of that. She needed a little time to settle herself before confronting him with her new image. She had had her hair cut in a short page-boy bob, with a deep fringe that seemed to change the whole proportion of her face. A treatment had done wonders for its condition, giving it a gloss that brought out the natural russet tints, and a loose perm to the roots had given it a lift that made it look twice as thick as before.

'I'll just drop you off,' said Helen breezily as she paused beside the surgery. 'I've got to get up to the school to pick up the kids.'

'Oh, yes, of course,' Josey smiled warmly. They had had a lovely day, and she felt that she had really made a friend in Tom's sister-in-law. 'Thank you for the lift.'

'No trouble! See you at Vanessa's, if not before.'

Collecting the pile of shopping bags from the back seat, Josey climbed out of the car. As soon as she opened the front door the two dogs bounded over to welcome her with a delight that nearly knocked her over. Quickly she slipped upstairs with her shopping and hid it away—it was a little foolish, she acknowledged wryly, but she wanted the dress to be a surprise to him.

There was still no sign of Tom when she went back downstairs, so she made herself a cup of coffee and took it through to the office. The cluttered little room had been transformed since he had agreed to let her tidy up. All the filing was done, and she had dusted his desk, and put a bowl of roses on it to brighten the place up. She wasn't sure if he had noticed how hard she had been working—he hadn't said a word about it.

She was just finishing the previous week's accounts when she heard the Land Rover draw up outside—she could recognise the engine's sound now as surely as Jethro. She heard him come in, and kept her head bent in concentration over her work.

The sound of his footsteps approaching made the tiny hairs at the back of her neck prickle, but though she sensed him standing in the doorway he didn't speak. After a moment she glanced up questioningly. He was leaning one wide shoulder against the door-frame, watching her, that grim, unreadable expression on his face.

'Is there anything wrong?' she asked, suddenly anxious.

'Oh . . . no.' He shrugged, his eyes drifting around the room. 'You've tidied up in here.'

'Only a little bit. I thought the roses . . . made it look nice. But I can take them away again if you don't like them.'

'No—they're fine. You've had your hair cut, too,' he added, almost as an afterthought. 'It looks nice.'

The compliment was almost grudgingly given, but somehow all the more genuine for that. She smiled up at him in surprise. 'Thank you. I had it done in town this afternoon.'

'Oh, yes. You went with Helen, didn't you? I expect you managed to clear out half the stocks of every dress-shop you found, between you, didn't you?'

'Well, not quite,' she responded, smiling in response to his friendly teasing. 'But we tried.'

He turned his eyes away from her abruptly, glancing down at the papers on the desk. 'How are you getting on with that?' he enquired.

'I've all but finished. It doesn't take long, once you get the hang of it. Why don't you use the computer?' she added, gesturing towards the large carton she had uncovered in the corner, still with its polystyrene packaging inside. 'That would take most of the hassle out of it.'

His eyes slid evasively away from hers. 'Oh, I can't be bothered with it,' he grunted impatiently. 'It's more trouble than it's worth.'

'I'm sure it wouldn't be, once you'd got the programs set up,' she persisted. 'It's just a matter of finding the right spreadsheet—or making up your own, if need be.'

'I've got enough to do, without messing about with all that.'

'But it would save you no end of time, once you'd put in the initial effort——'

'Will you stop interfering and trying to tell me how to run my own practice?' he exploded. 'Somehow I seemed to manage well enough before you came along.'

Her eyes sparked. 'I'm only trying to help,' she protested. 'If I can't make a simple suggestion ...!'

She rose to her feet to stalk from the room, but as she passed him he caught her by the wrist, turning her back to face him, and for one startling moment

their eyes locked in angry challenge. Then to her utter
surprise he laughed in wry self-mockery.

'I don't know how to use the damned thing,' he
confessed, almost sheepishly.

She stared at him, struggling to get her breathing
under control, her own anger abating swiftly as she
understood where his had come from. 'Well, why
didn't you just say so?' she asked mildly. 'It's nothing
to be ashamed of—lots of people have trouble learning
to use computers.'

That glorious smile shone out. 'I've tried, but it
just baffles me,' he confessed. 'I must be doing something wrong. Maybe you could teach me,' he added,
a glimmer of something she couldn't quite interpret
lurking in the depths of his hazel eyes.

'Of course.' He was still holding her wrist, and his
touch seemed to be burning her skin. Suddenly she
was acutely aware of him, of the subtle male muskiness of his skin, of the way his thick dark hair curled
over his ears. She tried to draw back, but he wouldn't
let her go.

A strange tension seemed to shimmer in the air between them, and she found herself drawn inexorably
closer to him. Her heartbeat was pounding in her
chest, making her blood swirl dizzyingly through her
veins. Slowly—infinitely slowly—his head bent over
hers, and their warm breath mingled.

Her lips parted on a soundless sigh. She could
hardly believe that this was happening. But as his
mouth melted over hers she closed her eyes, surrendering herself to the magic of the moment. Dream or
reality, she didn't care—she wasn't even sure she could
distinguish between the two.

His strong arms were around her, curving her supple body against the hard length of his. His lips were moving over hers, intoxicatingly, and his tongue was plundering deep into the sweetest softness of her mouth in an exploration that was flagrantly sensuous, stirring a helpless response inside her...

The ring of the bell in the surgery waiting-room broke them apart. Tom let her go abruptly. 'That'll be Bob, to fetch his dog,' he said, and went out without another glance in her direction.

Josey paused for a moment, trying to steady the rapid beating of her heart. What was happening? For the past couple of days he had been distant and cool, and she had almost begun to believe that she had imagined that kiss in the cottage. But now... those last few moments had certainly not been a product of her imagination—her lips still felt warm from his touch.

Maybe it was the new haircut, she thought wildly, or something to do with the confidence that had been returning to her all week with the general improvement in her health. Whatever it was, it was dangerous, because she didn't know how to handle it. She had forgotten.

Over the past few years she had come to see herself as some kind of female eunuch, devoid of all appeal for men. Now, very uncertainly, she was beginning to emerge from that chrysalis; and of all the people she could have chosen to get tangled up with at this point of her life Tom was the worst kind. She needed someone who would handle her bruised heart with care, someone who would be her friend and offer her security—not someone who would heat her blood to fever pitch at one moment, and the next turn her to ice with a harsh word, an impatient look.

It was time to do the sensible thing; to find a hotel, until her cottage was renovated and fit to live in. She should have done it days ago, but she had been lulled into a false sense of security after that brief incident at the cottage, able to convince herself that it had happened only because she had pushed him into losing his temper by talking about his ex-wife. But now the writing was on the wall. Only a fool would risk ignoring it.

Tom had brought Shep through from the house into the clinic, where his owners were waiting for him—the sturdy young farmer, his wife, a homely girl in a flower-printed dress, who regarded Josey with unabashed curiosity, and two small boys who were too eager to notice anything but their beloved pet, trotting through from the back room at Tom's heels, as if his life had never hung in the balance just a few short days ago.

'Shep! Is he all better?' they demanded, tumbling to their knees to hug the little dog, and gazing up at Tom as if he were Superman and Father Christmas all rolled into one.

'He's fine. But he mustn't romp around too much for a couple of days—you must remember that he's been very poorly.'

They nodded solemnly, stroking Shep's small shaggy head as he nuzzled in against them. 'Thank you,' they whispered, as if they had been handed a miracle.

Josey stood watching from the doorway of the office, a lump in her throat. It really did seem like a miracle, to be able to take that sad little bundle of fur that had been brought in suffering so much pain, and restore it to bright-eyed health.

'I'll give you some antibiotics,' Tom was saying to the farmer. 'Give him one in the morning, and one at night, and bring him in to see me on Monday.'

'Thanks, Tom.' He grinned down at his two sons, his emotions plain on his face. 'How much do I owe you?'

The two of them moved over to the desk to settle the account, and Josey smiled diffidently at the young woman. 'They're very fond of their dog, aren't they?' she remarked, trying to make some kind of conversation.

The farmer's wife looked faintly embarrassed at being addressed. 'Oh...yes, very,' she flustered. 'Come along now, you two, let's take him out to the car. 'Bye, Tom. Er—goodbye,' she added awkwardly to Josey.

'Goodbye.' She watched her usher the children out, a wistful smile curving her mouth. She was going to miss that little dog—in just a few days she had grown incredibly fond of him. Perhaps that was her trouble, she reflected wryly. She was looking for someone— anyone—to love; a sick dog...a bad-tempered, hard-to-please veterinary surgeon...

Tom seemed entirely unmoved—but then it must be an everyday incident for him. He stepped past her, careful—it seemed to her—not to brush too close, and went into the office, pulling open the desk drawer and dropping the folded cheque into a large cash-box.

'There.' He glanced up at her. 'I have some paperwork to do this evening,' he added brusquely. 'I'll see you later.'

She nodded, her heart empty. That gulf was there between them again, a channel too wide for her to cross. And perhaps it was better if she didn't try, she reflected wryly. There was nothing for her on the other side.

Unfortunately Tom's prediction about the difficulty she would find in booking a hotel room proved accurate. The best she could manage was a suggestion that there might be a possibility after the weekend. So Saturday found her still in her little oak-beamed room beneath the eaves of Tom's cottage.

Since Wednesday the two of them had been moving carefully around each other, as distant and polite as strangers, scrupulously avoiding any sort of contact. It was like living on top of a powder-keg, never quite sure when a stray spark would blow the whole thing sky-high.

And now it was Saturday evening—time to get ready for Vanessa's party. If only she could think of some excuse not to go! She stood looking at her reflection in the old-fashioned cheval-glass in the corner of the room, wondering anxiously if she had chosen the right dress.

It was quite something. Of vampish black satin, with a clinging, ruched bodice cut low across the curve of her breasts, and a skirt that hugged the length of her slender legs, it would not have looked out of place at a film première. It had its own matching bolero, and she had bought a pair of sandals, with very high heels, to go with it.

Fortunately she had had the presence of mind to throw some of her jewellery into her suitcase when she had left Colin, so she had a selection gold chains and earrings to choose from. She went for simplicity—a plain serpentine chain around her throat, and gold hoops in her ears.

Was it *too* glamorous? What if everyone else was in casual clothes? But Helen had helped her choose this, and she trusted Helen's assurance that Vanessa's midsummer ball was an occasion of the most sumptuous sartorial upstaging on the part of all the women present.

As she walked down the stairs she felt a surge of reassurance at seeing Tom in a formal black dinner-jacket. It looked good on him, he whom she had never seen in anything but hard-working denim shirts and well-worn jeans. It was moulded beautifully over his wide shoulders, subtly distinguishing the powerful maleness of his body.

He was on the telephone, speaking to Hugh, but he half turned as he heard her walking down the stairs, glancing up at her. His eyes widened in surprise, and he choked on some inarticulate sound in his throat. 'I . . . I'm sorry, Hugh—what was that you said?'

Josey walked on down to the kitchen, absently stroking Jethro's head as he came to welcome her. She could feel Tom's eyes follow her across the room, and her heart began to flutter in nervous uncertainty. Was the dress perhaps a little too much after all? She had nothing else suitable to change into—she had bought only a few casual clothes on the rest of her shopping-trip.

Tom finished his conversation, and put down the telephone, and, drawing a deep steadying breath, she turned to face him. 'Well?' she enquired, her voice a little shaky. 'Will I do?'

'Oh, yes . . .' He let his gaze travel slowly down over the length of her slender body, registering undisguised appreciation. 'Yes, you'll certainly do.'

She could feel her cheeks growing warm. 'Thank you,' she managed—she didn't trust herself to say anything more.

He reached out to pick up his car keys from the cluttered mantelpiece. 'We'd better be off,' he said, his voice oddly husky. 'We don't want to be late.'

CHAPTER SIX

THERE was silence in the car as Tom and Josey drove the short distance to Vanessa's. The sexual tension that had been smouldering between them for the past few days had come to the surface with a vengeance tonight. And, even as Josey felt a small glow of satisfaction that at last she had found some chink in that ice-wall with which he surrounded himself, she was aware of a small quiver of nervous apprehension inside her. Where, exactly, was this going to lead?

Cottisham Manor was a substantial stone-built house, a little beyond the village, set in a large, well-kept garden. In the golden glow of the midsummer evening it had a prosperous air about it. Vanessa had done well for herself, Josey reflected, even if she had married her baronet mainly to save face after losing Tom.

They arrived at the same moment as Helen and her husband, parking the Land Rover behind their car. Like Hugh, Donald bore a striking family resemblance to Tom, but five extra years and the contentment of a happy family life had softened his features and broadened his waistline.

He greeted her with a warm handshake, but he was a man of few words. Helen, however, was bubbling with excitement. 'You look great,' she whispered with gleeful satisfaction as they walked up to the front door. 'Vanessa's really going to feel as if her nose has been put out of joint.'

It was Vanessa herself who opened the door. One glimpse of her hostess—shimmering in vivid flamingo-pink silk—was enough to finally reassure Josey that she herself was not overdressed. She had hung back a little as Helen—smart but not spectacular in green figured silk—went forward to collect an insincere kiss of welcome from her cousin, but Tom took her hand, and drew her forward into the light spilling from the porch.

The effect was all she could have wanted. Tom had held on to her hand for just a little longer than was strictly necessary, a point which was not missed by the gimlet-eyed blonde. Nor was the sheer stylish elegance of the dress. The smile that greeted them as they stepped up to the threshold looked as if it had been set in concrete.

'Good evening, Vanessa.' Tom's voice held just a trace of sardonic amusement, as if he was well aware of the edge of rivalry between the two women. 'Nice of you to have invited us.'

'Oh...yes... Do come in.' Vanessa was swift to recover her poise, aided by the finely-honed talents of the perfect hostess. 'Gerry's serving drinks in the drawing-room—you know the way, Tom.'

'Thank you.'

He took Josey's arm again in a deliberately possessive grip, and steered her into the house. As she passed Vanessa, the two women exchanged thin smiles. There was no chance of melting the ice there, Josey acknowledged with a trace of regret. But she had to admit that it did wonders for her self-confidence to know that the other woman was jealous of her.

The house was furnished with expensive good taste. If some of the Sheraton was reproduction, it was very good, and the layered swags of heavy jacquard satin covering the windows were perfectly colour co-ordinated with the wall-paper. An interior designer couldn't have done better.

There was already quite a gathering in the impressive drawing-room, but as they entered Josey was conscious of a sudden lull in the conversation, and sensed that people were covertly watching her—she could feel the curiosity of their eyes resting on her. So *this* was the woman who was living with Tom Quinn.

The role of scarlet woman was an unaccustomed one for her, but she resolutely hid her embarrassment behind a mask of cool dignity. She really didn't have much choice, she reflected wryly. She could hardly stand here and announce to the assembled company, 'It's not what you think.'

And Tom wasn't exactly helping matters, standing so close behind her like that, as possessive as a dog with a bone. No one looking at them would doubt that they were lovers. A flicker of anger sparked in her eyes. It was all very well for *him*—a little intriguing gossip would probably do his reputation no harm at all. But she didn't doubt that she would be judged by quite another standard, and in this close-knit rural community that could make it even more difficult for her to be accepted.

Was *no one* going to approach them? She was so relieved when a nice-looking young man, fair-haired and blue-eyed, came forward with an eager smile to welcome them that she almost hugged him. It took little to guess that this was their host.

'Hi, Tom, how are you doing?' he exclaimed, slapping him on the shoulder with the vigour of an overgrown puppy. 'Glad you could make it.'

'Hello, Gerald,' Tom responded genially. 'Josey, this is Gerald Fordham-Jones. Gerald, Josey Rutherford.'

He extended his hand in informal politeness, though his eyes clearly betrayed his admiration. 'Good evening,' he greeted her eagerly. 'I'm delighted to meet you.'

'How do you do?' Josey couldn't help but smile in response. So this was Vanessa's husband. He seemed a pleasant young man—Helen had perhaps exaggerated a *little* in describing him as chinless. His boyish manner made him seem quite young—Josey wondered if he could be older than thirty. 'I'm afraid I can't shake hands,' she added lightly, holding up her injured wrist, still in its cast. 'It's my war-wound.'

'And don't you dare damage my handiwork,' added a laughing voice beside her. 'Hello, Mrs Rutherford. How are you now?'

Josey turned, to smile up at the young doctor who had set her wrist at the hospital. 'Oh, please, call me Josey,' she insisted warmly. 'And my wrist is very much better, thank you. I can even move my fingers now—look!'

'That's very good,' he approved, his eyes still studying her as if he couldn't quite believe the transformation that had taken place in less than two weeks. 'And you're certainly looking a great deal better,' he added, an entirely unprofessional interest in his voice.

Josey laughed as she accepted the compliment. She had almost forgotten how pleasant it could be to indulge in this kind of light-hearted flirtation; and, if

Tom didn't like it, it served him right for treating her like an irritating nuisance for the past ten days.

Tom wasn't the only one who didn't like it— Vanessa, noticing who was the centre of all this male attention, moved in swiftly to intervene. 'Darling, you haven't given Tom and Josey a drink,' she chided her husband in a brittle show of affection. 'What will you have? Champagne cocktail? Or something stronger?'

'Just plain mineral water for me,' Tom said. 'Josey?'

Vanessa's laugh had a sarcastic bite. 'Oh, don't tell me you're going to be teetotal tonight, Tom! You're not on call, are you?'

'No. But I promised Hugh I'd be available if anything cropped up that was too much for him to handle, and I'd prefer to keep a clear head just in case.'

'Oh, phoo!' Vanessa pouted. She turned blithely to Josey. 'He's such a bore—so dedicated! But then you'll find out what you'll have to put up with.'

Josey lifted one eyebrow a fraction of an inch. 'Will I?' she responded evenly.

Her cool response left Vanessa fluttering foolishly, and Josey silently chalked up another point to herself. It was really rather foolish to be playing this game of one-upmanship, she acknowledged wryly, but she seemed to be caught in it whether she liked it or not. And it would be unwise to underestimate her opponent, she warned herself with timely caution. Vanessa had more practice than she had in being a bitch.

And indeed Vanessa recovered her composure quickly. 'Simon, please fetch a mineral water for Mr Quinn, and whatever Mrs Rutherford would like,' she instructed the formally dressed butler. 'Josey, I just love that dress,' she added, her tone primed with acid. 'Of course, you can get away with it, having nothing up top. If I were to wear it, I'd be in constant danger of having a boob pop out!'

She laughed girlishly, slanting Tom a coy look to ensure that he was noticing the difference between her own alluring curves and Josey's deficiency. But Josey's confidence was supported by a reassuring wink from Helen, who made a small gesture with her hand like a cat's claws. If Vanessa felt the need to make catty remarks, she must be feeling distinctly threatened. Her mind shuffled and rejected a number of witty responses, settling instead for an enigmatic smile.

'Well, everyone, what are we doing still indoors on such a lovely evening?' Vanessa was hyped-up and on edge, like a sparkler about to burn itself out. 'Why don't we go out into the garden?'

'Have you been out to look at your cottage yet?' the doctor enquired of Josey as they made their way outside.

She nodded. 'Yes. Most of it isn't in bad condition, but I'm afraid the kitchen——'

'It will need a lot of work to make it habitable,' cut in Tom, his abrupt tone making it clear that he was terminating the conversation. His hand on Josey's arm was like steel as he steered her away.

Her anger flared. 'How dare you?' she demanded in a gritted undervoice as soon as they were out of earshot. 'I was talking.'

He glared down at her, his eyes hard and angry. 'Is this how you always behave?' he demanded. 'Flaunting yourself with every man in the room?'

'Don't be ridiculous,' she threw back at him. 'I wasn't flaunting myself.'

'Let's dance.'

A trio of musicians was playing on one corner of the wide terrace, and already several couples were dancing. Before she could argue, Josey found herself swung into Tom's arms, and he was moving her slowly to the music, holding her so close that if anyone had been harbouring any doubts about the nature of their relationship they would have been instantly dispelled. Only a man's mistress would allow herself to be held so intimately in public.

But she couldn't do anything about it. Beneath the civilised veneer afforded by his elegant dinner-jacket was a primeval male strength that she knew she couldn't fight. No caveman could have asserted his rights over his mate more aggressively, and it was quite certain that no one was going to challenge him.

And deep inside her some treacherous core of purely feminine submissiveness was betraying her, melting her into a willing surrender. She closed her eyes, letting herself drift into a dream. The fragrance of roses and honeysuckle was soft on the evening air, and she was in danger of falling in love ...

In the summer twilight, the gardens of Cottisham Manor were a perfect place for lovers to stroll. Wide green lawns, dotted with trees, ran down to a quiet stream, fringed with reed beds that whispered as they swayed in the evening breeze. A romantic hump-backed bridge of grey stone spanned the slow water.

Romance, Josey mused wryly—she was a fool to even think of it. Oh, Tom wanted her—he had made that abundantly clear to anyone who had cared to watch them while they were dancing. But she had no illusions—where Tom Quinn was concerned, wanting had nothing to do with love.

They stood on the bridge, leaning on the parapet, watching the lazy drift of the weeds in the water below. Though they were a foot apart, it was impossible to ignore that powerful masculinity that emanated from him, without any apparent effort on his part. She slanted a wary glance at his profile, hard and arrogant in the gathering dusk, giving nothing away.

'I . . . I was just thinking,' she began haltingly. 'I'm really a lot better now—I can even use my hand a bit. There's. . . really no reason for me to stay at your place any longer.' He didn't answer, and she stumbled on awkwardly. 'I could probably find a hotel or something by Monday.'

He turned his head to look at her, his eyes filled with lazy mockery. 'Why are you in such a hurry to move out all of a sudden?' he enquired. 'Are you afraid I'll find you so irresistible that I'll creep into your room in the middle of the night and force you to surrender to my wicked demands?'

'No, of course not!' She was glad of the shadows of evening to hide the deepening pink of her cheeks. 'It's just. . . you must know what everyone's thinking.'

'I'm not psychic,' he responded, obstinately unhelpful.

She had to swallow hard before she could force the words out. 'They all think we're having an affair.'

'So?'

'Oh, it's all very well for you,' she protested. 'But I want them to like me. I want to make friends here—this is going to be my home.'

He scoffed in mocking cynicism. 'Oh, we're back to that again, are we?' he taunted. 'You won't stay here. I give you three months, at the outside. Come September you'll be bored stiff, and dying to get back to London.'

'You seem very sure you're right,' she choked out.

'I know I'm right. But in the meantime, since you say everyone's already gossiping, neither of us has anything to lose, have we?' He was moving towards her, reaching for her with an intent that was signalled in his eyes.

She drew back, turning her head aside. 'No, Tom,' she whispered. 'Please...'

He laughed softly. 'Are you trying to tell me that you don't want me to kiss you?' he queried with a twist of derisive humour. 'Don't lie, Josey. Your eyes give away too many secrets.'

He drew her into his arms, his will almost over-powering hers. But some stronger part of her was still resisting, knowing the price of surrender. She put her hands between them, holding him away, her head still turned so that he couldn't see her face, couldn't en-slave her with the mesmerising power of his eyes.

'No,' she insisted, though her voice was cracking. 'It's not...' As she struggled to find the words, some-thing down in the water caught her eye; a cardboard box, drifting on the slow current—but it was moving in an odd, erratic sort of way, as if there was some-thing alive inside. 'What's that...?'

She broke free of him, and ran down to the river-bank, glad to snatch at any excuse to escape. But there was a distinct sound coming from the box now, a dis-tressed squeaking. It had snared up against a bank of reeds, and was beginning to sink.

'There's something in there!' she cried, heedless of the sudden startled attention of the other guests, standing around on the terrace sipping Vanessa's crisp champagne. 'Oh, quick—it's going to drown.'

Without even thinking, she plunged out into the reeds, struggling as the mud sucked her down, impatiently abandoning her elegant sandals to a watery grave. Her new dress, dragging in the water, was being ruined, but she didn't care. With one outstretched hand she managed to reach the box, but the cardboard was so sodden that she feared it would disintegrate if she tried to pull it closer.

A longer arm than hers reached past her, and Tom caught the box, lifting it clear as it began to slip beneath the water. With a sob of relief she stepped back, accepting the helping hands that drew her up on to the grassy bank. Tom set the box down, and with a scrabbling noise the lid opened, and a tiny head popped out.

'It's a puppy!' Josey fell to her knees, taking up the tiny thing in her hands. It was mostly white, with brown patches on its head, and droopy little ears. Its eyes were just open, a misty blue, and its body was plump and soft. 'It isn't very old,' she cried, holding it close against her chest to warm it, not caring that it was dripping wet. 'How could anyone do a cruel thing like that?'

'All too easily, I'm afraid,' Tom responded gruffly. 'That's the only one out of the litter that's made it.'

'Oh, poor little things.' The tears rose to her eyes, and she stroked the tiny trembling body in her arms, unable to watch as he carried the box away to a deeper part of the bank, and let the waters take it. Around her a sympathetic crowd had gathered, and Helen had come to her side, kneeling down with her.

'Josey, you're all wet,' she reminded her gently.

'And you've ruined that dress,' added Vanessa with a scathing satisfaction that would have stung had Josey been taking any notice.

Josey just shook her head in total unconcern. 'Oh, the dress doesn't matter!' She looked up to find Tom. 'Please, have a look at him,' she begged anxiously, holding out the puppy to him. 'Is he going to be all right?'

He bent down beside her, taking the trembling little body and giving it a brief examination. '*She's* going to be fine,' he promised, handing it back to her. 'All she needs is warmth and food, and a bit of tender loving care.'

Quickly she slipped off her silk bolero, wrapping the puppy up in it and cuddling it close, murmuring to it soothingly as she rose to her feet. 'How old do you think she is?' she asked.

'I'd say about three weeks,' he guessed. 'People often dump them at that age, just when the bitch's milk is beginning to dry up, and they're going to have the bother of weaning them.' He looked closely at the puppy again. 'She looks as if she's got a fair bit of Jack Russell in her, and heaven knows what else. What are you going to do with her?'

'Keep her, of course!' The little pup had snuggled down against her contentedly. 'She's going to need a name,' she mused. 'What can I call her?'

'If it was a boy you could call it Moses,' suggested Helen.

'Yes, but that wouldn't do for a girl . . .' Suddenly the pup sneezed. 'Oh, dear—has she got a cold?'

Tom shook his head. 'Dogs don't get colds,' he assured her.

The pup sneezed again, looking comically puzzled. Josey cuddled her close, laughing happily, her whole heart captured. 'I think you must have got some pepper up your nose. Hey, that's what I'll call her,' she added decisively. 'Pepper.'

'Pepper?' Tom slanted her a look of sardonic amusement. 'Well, at least it's not too fancy.' He took off his jacket and dropped it around her shoulders. 'Come on, then—we'd better get it home in the warm, and let it have something to eat. And you'd better get that dress off too, before *you* catch cold.'

Vanessa glared at Josey, knowing exactly who to blame for taking Tom away from her party so early. 'You're leaving, then?' she asked, a sharp edge in her voice.

Tom flickered her a glance of dry amusement. 'I'm afraid so. But thank you for a very pleasant evening,' he added, mockingly polite. 'Goodnight, everyone.'

'Yes, goodnight,' put in Josey, smiling round shyly at the circle of well-wishers—all the disapproval and suspicion she had sensed before seemed to have magically evaporated, and people she had never met before were wishing her a warm goodnight.

'Goodnight.' Helen leaned over and kissed her cheek in a quite natural gesture of sisterly affection. 'I'll pop round tomorrow—maybe I'll bring the kids round to see Pepper, if that's OK?'

'Oh, yes—of course,' Josey felt a warm glow. 'That would be lovely.'

They walked round the side of the house, to where Tom had parked the Land Rover. The little puppy had fallen asleep, and didn't even stir as Josey shifted her from hand to hand so that she could put her seatbelt on. She stroked the plump little body gently with one finger, feeling the tiny heart pattering so fast.

'Oh, she's so sweet,' she murmured. 'I've never had a dog before. What should I feed her on?'

'There's some milk-powder in the clinic,' Tom responded, starting the car. 'That'll do her for the first few days, maybe with a little beef-broth. Then she can start with a little oatmeal or some strained baby-food. She'll need feeding every three hours,' he warned. 'And you'll probably have to get up in the night to her, as well.'

'That's OK—I don't mind.'

'You'll have to make very sure you keep her out of the clinic,' he added. 'It'll be weeks before she can have her injections, and until then there could be a risk of her picking up an infection.'

She nodded seriously. She hadn't expected that the gap in her heart, left by her unfulfilled longing for a baby, could be filled by a warm little puppy. But as the tiny thing stirred, opening her small pink mouth in a wide, wide yawn, she knew that she had found something to love very nearly as much as she would have loved a baby.

They drew up outside the clinic, and Tom came round to open her door for her. 'Here, give her to me,' he offered as she stepped out of the car. 'I'll mix her up some milk. You'd better go and get out of that dress before you catch your death of cold.'

'You're wet too,' she reminded him, noticing with a small stab of guilt that his trousers were muddy and wet to above the knees. 'How come your shoes are clean, though?'

'I had the presence of mind to kick mine off before I went wading in the mud,' he informed her with a flicker of dry humour. 'I'm afraid you've seen the last of yours.'

'They got stuck,' she explained blithely. 'Never mind—they weren't very comfortable anyway.'

He opened the front door, scolding the collie as he came bounding over excitedly to see what he held in his hands. 'Down, Jethro. Yes, it's a puppy, but she's too small for you to play with yet.'

Josey smiled to herself. He had such an easy way with animals; it was a pity he couldn't spare a little more of that warmth for human beings. Wrapped up in his jacket, so large that it swamped her slender frame, she suddenly found herself remembering what it had been like to be wrapped up in his arms, as they had danced on the terrace...

But she didn't want to think about that just now—there were too many complications. She would think about it later, when she was alone, after she had seen to little Pepper. 'I'll...go and change,' she said quickly, and hurried away up the stairs.

Swiftly she stripped off the sodden dress, tossing it to the floor. It was almost certainly beyond repair, but she didn't care—it had been worth it to save the little puppy's life. Poor little mite—the way it had snuggled against her, so trusting... It was just a baby, but already life had been so cruel to it. Well, it was safe now, she vowed resolutely. Whatever it took to look after it, she wouldn't grudge.

She had a quick shower to wash the caked mud off her legs and feet, and then pulling on Tom's old red tartan dressing-gown, she went back down to the kitchen. Tom had changed too, into a dark blue woollen dressing-gown, and had tucked the puppy into the front of it to keep warm—her tiny head was peeping nervously out at the world that had so recently been such an alarming place. He had found a large carton for her to sleep in, and was lining it with newspaper and a piece of cosy therma-fibre, as Jethro sat at his feet watching with concentrated interest.

'Can I take her?' Josey asked, holding out her hands.

'Here.' As he extricated the tiny thing from his dressing-gown she squeaked in protest, but quickly settled into Josey's arms. 'I'll go and get some milk-powder from the clinic.'

'Right.' Gently she lowered the puppy into her new sleeping box. 'There you are, Pepper,' she coaxed softly, stroking the drooping little head. 'You'll be as safe as houses in there.' Jethro leaned up to peer into the box, his nose snuffling, and Josey stroked him too.

It was only when she heard the door close that she realised that Tom hadn't left the room at once—he must have been standing watching her. How dearly she would love to know what he was thinking! Did he think she was being stupidly sentimental over the puppy, like a typical city girl?

'Well, I don't care,' she murmured to the two dogs. 'Let him think what he likes.'

Carefully she lifted the carton down from the table, and knelt on the floor beside it, watching as the pup sniffed her way cautiously around her new quarters, having a little difficulty as her tiny claws kept snagging on the fibre of her bedding. She seemed to find it satisfactory, however, because she plopped down in one corner and promptly went to sleep.

Tom came back a few moments later, to find her still kneeling rapt over the box, watching the puppy snuffling gently in her sleep. He laughed softly as he crossed the room. 'You're hooked, aren't you?' he teased gently.

'She's such a pretty little thing,' Josey argued. 'And so tiny. Look at her little claws. And she's fast asleep.'

He came over, and knelt down beside her to peer into the box. 'Well, she's soon made herself comfortable,' he remarked with a touch of humour. 'Here, tuck this hot-water bottle under the therma-fibre, and see if you can get her to take some of this milk.'

The puppy was so sleepy that she didn't really want to stir. Patiently Josey persuaded her to take a few drops of the warm powdered milk from the syringe that Tom had given her, but the misty little eyes were closing, and the tiny pink mouth opened in another very wide yawn.

'Leave her, then, if she isn't hungry,' Tom advised. 'She's had a hard day.'

Josey looked up at him enquiringly. 'Do you know who it was that put them in the water?' she asked, a hard edge in her voice.

'I've got a pretty good idea,' he confirmed grimly. 'Don't worry—I'll sort them out.'

'I'd like to do the same to them,' she declared, her jaw set. 'I don't know what they deserve for being so cruel.'

He smiled in understanding, and stroked a soothing hand down over her hair. She felt a sudden flood of warmth through her veins, and lowered her eyes quickly, not sure how to interpret the touch. But as he slid his hand round under her chin, lifting her face to his, she felt as if her heart had stopped beating.

Those hazel eyes were so compellingly intense, she felt as though she could drown in them...

For a long, tense moment he gazed down at her, searching her face, almost—it seemed to her—fighting the urge to kiss her. But some instinct older than Eve had caught her in its spell, and almost of their own volition her fingers grasped the lapels of his dressing-gown, drawing him towards her. And slowly, almost reluctantly, his head bent towards hers, and their mouths melted together.

His kiss was so exquisitely tender, rousing a sweet turmoil within, making her forget all her doubts and reservations. His lips were warm and firm on hers, coaxing and inciting her to respond, his languorous tongue swirling over all the secret, sensitive membranes deep within her mouth, stirring fires inside her that she had no idea how to control.

His strong arms curved her fiercely against him, crushing her tender breasts against the hard wall of his chest, and as she clung to him she felt the heat of his body, the hard strength of his muscles, so easily able to overpower her. But even as she recognised how very vulnerable she was, she knew also that he would never use his physical strength to take what he wanted. That wasn't his way. Not that that was much help, she reflected wildly—he didn't need to overpower her physically when he was so very expert in other means of persuasion!

She was so lost to all reason that she didn't even protest when he slid his hand inside her dressing-gown to find the warm naked curve of her breast. Some part of her mind registered dimly that she shouldn't be permitting this, but he was kissing her into submission, claiming all that she had to offer and then

demanding more, plundering every secret corner of
her mouth with a hungry demand that wouldn't be
denied.

And his touch was so magical, his sensitive fingers
caressing her in slow, tantalising circles, teasing the
tender bud of her nipple until it ripened into his palm,
and she was aching with longing, a soft pleading sound
in her throat as their lips broke apart.

His mouth was dusting hot, scorching kisses across
her face, finding the fluttering pulse beneath her
delicate temple, lingering sensuously in the dainty shell
of her ear. The wrap of her dressing-gown had come
loose, and he pulled it apart, his arms folding around
her slender body and curving her against him, naked,
her body still soft and warm from her bath.

'I want you, Josey,' he whispered fiercely, his breath
hot against her cheek.

'Yes...' she answered blindly, her will surrendering totally to his. Her head swam dizzily as he
scooped her up in his strong arms, as if she weighed
nothing at all, and carried her up the stairs to his
bedroom.

His bed was big and comfortable; as he laid her
down on it, Josey felt as if she was floating on a
dream. She reached up for him, drawing him down
with her, and he laughed softly, low in his throat, as
his mouth claimed hers again, and his caressing hands
stroked possessively over her smooth skin.

His dressing-gown too had fallen apart, and instinctively she wrapped her arms around his powerful
body, glorying in the heat of his skin, the smooth
hardness of his well-disciplined muscles, the wonder-
fully masculine scattering of rough dark hair across
his wide chest.

His scorching kisses were following the path of his hands, the slight rasp of his jaw delicious against her silken skin as he ventured down into the soft valley between her breasts. Instinctively her spine curved towards him, offering herself to him in wanton invitation.

And then at last his hot mouth found the sweet focus of one succulent nipple, lapping it with his sensuous tongue, and taking it deep into his mouth to suckle with a hungry rhythm, making her gasp for breath, her head tipping back and her whole body yielding to him.

She was helpless; she had never known an experience like this before, had never known that such sensations existed. Colin had never troubled with such caresses—he had judged his expertise purely on the basis of duration, expecting from her only passive compliance, and it had been more of a relief than a disappointment when he had begun to lose interest in her, within months of their marriage.

The memory of what it had been like came thudding back into her mind like a flood of ice water, just as Tom's hand moved down over the smooth plane of her stomach to gently part her thighs. Abruptly the fires inside her died, and she pulled away from him, almost falling off the bed.

'Josey...?'

He reached for her, puzzled, and she escaped quickly, standing up and wrapping her dressing-gown quickly around her body, a sick knot of reaction in the pit of her stomach.

'What the hell...?' Tom sat up, a dangerous anger flaring in his eyes. 'Is this some kind of game?' he demanded harshly.

Josey backed uneasily away from him. 'I'm sorry,' she whispered. 'I just . . . I can't . . . I . . .' How could she ever find the words to explain? 'I'm still married,' she blurted out, clutching at that feeble excuse with a kind of desperation.

'I know that,' he grated impatiently. 'But you're in the middle of getting a divorce—and, if what you've told me is true, the bastard hardly deserves your unswerving fidelity.'

'I know. It's just . . . I know I'm being silly, but . . .'

'All right—you've made yourself perfectly clear,' he snapped, rising to his feet and tying up his dressing-gown. 'There's no need to act as if you think I'm going to rape you.'

'I didn't think that.' She hung her head. How could she tell him what had gone wrong? She didn't even know herself why it had happened. One moment everything had been fine, all her responses had been working perfectly normally, and then . . . *click*—she had switched off. Colin's accusing voice had come back to echo in her brain. Frigid.

'I'll put the kettle on,' suggested Tom, his voice taut with exasperation. 'I think we could both do with a cup of coffee.'

'Yes. I . . . I'm sorry.' She trailed after him down the stairs to the kitchen. 'I think it would be better if I move out as soon as possible,' she offered, her voice unsteady. 'I'll try to find a hotel on Monday.'

He laughed drily. 'If you think you can find a hotel that's willing to take in a three-week old puppy while you house-train it,' he pointed out.

'Oh . . .' She hadn't thought of little Pepper, fast asleep in the corner of her cardboard box. Of course no hotel would accept such a liability. But she couldn't bear to part with her, not now she'd found her. But if she stayed here... She lifted her eyes to Tom's face, anxiously seeking to know what he was thinking.

'Yes, you can stay on here,' he answered her unspoken question tersely. 'And you don't have to worry—I won't demand that you pay your rent by lying on your back.'

CHAPTER SEVEN

WELL, she couldn't complain that Tom hadn't kept his promise, Josey reflected wryly. It had been nearly three weeks now, and he had been scrupulous in not coming near her. It was almost impossible to believe that two people could share the same house and stay so far apart. Of course, he was very busy—at least that was what he said. He was hardly at home.

At least she had Pepper for company. The puppy was growing into a bright-eyed little bundle of mischief, wanting to explore everything and sometimes far too bold for her own good. She had already got herself stuck behind the fridge, and Josey and Vi had had to manhandle it out of the way to set her free.

And of course there was Helen. The two of them had become close friends already; Helen would drop in most days, sometimes bringing her children with her. And it was through Helen that she had met Tom's parents. Helen had insisted that she should come to lunch one Sunday.

Josey had been a little wary at first. What would Tom's parents think of her, appearing out of the blue and apparently living with their son? What sort of explanation had Tom given them? 'I don't know,' she had demurred. 'Tom . . . might not like it.'

'Why on earth shouldn't he?' Helen had demanded.

'Well, you know, it isn't as if . . . I mean, we're not . . .'

'Never mind what he says,' Helen had insisted. 'You're coming—Sunday. And if my bone-headed brother-in-law won't bring you, I'll come and fetch you myself.'

In the event, Tom *had* agreed, with evident reluctance, to take her. The atmosphere in the car as they drove over had been strained, to say the least, but Josey had adopted a policy of ignoring him when he was in this kind of mood—she had found that it was the best way. She wasn't going to let him know how much it hurt.

The Quinn farmhouse was charming—a long, low, rambling structure that had clearly been added to by successive generations, the different parts blended into a harmonious whole through the use of the local grey flint stone. Helen's three children were at the gate, waiting to open it for them as they drove in.

'Have you brought Pepper?' demanded Sara, the youngest, scrambling up to the car. 'Nanna's dying to see her.'

'Of course I've brought her,' Josey confirmed, smiling as the children mobbed her. 'Steady, now—don't get her too excited.'

She put the puppy into Sara's arms, and the child hugged her carefully, running into the house to show her grandmother at once. Tom slanted her a sardonic look that she couldn't quite interpret, and led the way into the house.

The door opened straight into a large family kitchen. This was clearly the hub of the house, a large, cosy room with a quarry-tiled floor covered with a well-worn rug, and a gleaming black Aga cooker in the chimney. The rich smell of the roasting Sunday joint filled the air.

Josey hesitated for a second in the doorway, but Helen came forward to draw her in. 'Ah, you made it—good!' She flickered an enquiring glance towards Tom, but his face remained an enigmatic mask. 'Come and meet the family—well, you already know Don, of course, and Hugh.'

'Of course.' Josey greeted the two men seated at the big table with a warm smile.

'And this is my mother-in-law,' added Helen with obvious affection.

Josey wasn't quite sure what she had expected of Tom's mother. What she met was a tall, handsome woman with thick greying hair, caught back in a common-sense bun, who extended a friendly hand. 'Hello, Josey. I've been looking forward to meeting you—but then I've heard so much about you. I feel as if I know you already.'

Somehow Josey managed a smile, wondering wildly what on earth she *had* heard. 'H...hello, Mrs Quinn,' she murmured shyly, accepting the proffered hand.

'Oh, call me Phyllis, please! Your father's down in the stables,' she added to Tom as he kissed her cheek. 'Saffron foaled last night. Why don't you go down and take a look.'

'Oh, yes—you must come and see the foal, Josey,' the children insisted excitedly. 'He's just supercalifragilistic!'

'I'd love to,' she agreed, smiling down at them. 'But Pepper had better stay here.'

'Don't worry—I'll keep an eye on her,' Tom's mother assured her. 'I've reared many an orphan litter in my time, I can tell you! She'll be warm enough by the stove.'

Josey smiled. 'Thank you. She'll probably go straight back to sleep, anyway—she was playing before we came out.'

'Almost like having a baby, isn't it?' the older woman chuckled as they bent together to settle the little pup on an old cushion beside the warm Aga.

Josey felt her cheeks flame scarlet. Was that what she was doing—sublimating her frustrated maternal urges in caring for a puppy, when what she really wanted was a baby? And with a small shock she realised that her yearning for a baby, that she had learned to live with for so long, had taken on a treacherous twist. Somehow it now included Tom in the process.

Fortunately she had her back to Tom, but his mother hadn't missed the give-away signs. She smiled with an extra warmth. 'Go on down and have a look at the foal,' she urged. 'Tom will show you the way.'

Josey wished the floor would open up and swallow her. She really shouldn't have come—his mother was bound to get the wrong impression of their relationship. Didn't Tom realise that? Why hadn't he said something to put her right?

To her relief, Mrs Quinn had turned back to Tom. 'What a wicked thing to do, trying to drown them like that,' she exclaimed. 'Do you have any idea who it was, Tom?'

He nodded. 'I've told them if they can't afford to have their bitch spayed to bring her down to the surgery and I'll do it for nothing,' he said grimly.

His mother nodded approval. 'Far better that than to have them do that kind of thing. Some people just shouldn't be allowed to keep a dog.'

'Quite,' he agreed. 'Well, do you want to come and see this foal?' he added brusquely to Josey. He cast a disparaging eye at her smartly polished court shoes.

'You'd better be careful across the yard—it's likely to be muddy.'

'Here, put my wellies on,' offered Helen quickly. 'You should have warned her, Tom.'

He strode out into the yard, ignoring them both. Josey took a deep, steadying breath, and then smiled. 'Thanks, Helen,' she responded, trying hard to pretend that nothing was wrong.

The stables were on the far side of the farmyard. An early shower of rain had left the ground muddy, and her city shoes would indeed have been very unsuitable for picking her way across it. The children skipped along beside her eagerly, little Sara clinging to her hand.

Like his two sons, Donald Quinn Senior was a big, handsome man. He was wearing workmanlike cord jeans, tucked into the top of his rolled-down wellington boots, and he stood on no ceremony in his greetings. 'Hello, there, Josey. Come down to see the horses, have you? Do you ride?'

'No,' she admitted wistfully. 'I wish I could.'

'Ah—you'd best get Tom to teach you, then,' he advised easily, plainly sharing his wife's assumptions. 'Eh, Tom?'

'Oh...I...couldn't at the moment, anyway,' Josey stammered, quickly covering for Tom's lack of response. 'Not until my wrist's better.'

It was warm in the stable, the air sweet with the smell of fresh hay. Several of the stalls were occupied. Josey had never been this close to horses before, and when a huge head appeared above her shoulder, gazing at her curiously, she started aside.

'It's all right,' Tom assured her drily, stroking the horse's head. 'This is Gypsy. She won't hurt you.'

Somewhat uncertainly Josey moved closer. It had been more surprise than fear that had caused her reaction, and cautiously she put up her hand to stroke the sleek black neck. 'Hello, Gypsy,' she murmured softly.

The horse whiffled softly, turning her great head towards her. 'She likes you,' remarked Mr Quinn, sounding pleased. 'But she won't do for you if you're a novice—she could be a bit of a handful. You'd be best with our Saffron here—by the time your wrist is OK, she'll be ready to go out again.'

He gestured to her to come and look into the end stall, where he was attending to a fine-looking bay mare. As Tom approached the horse must have scented him, coming forward at once, proudly showing off the gangling young foal at her side.

'Well, aren't you a clever girl, then?' Tom flattered her, admiring her baby. 'Looks a nice healthy youngster,' he added to his father.

'Aye. That's the second good foal we've had off her. And she's a good mother, too—no problems in that department.'

Josey was captivated by the young foal. Its legs looked almost too slender to support its body, and it clung shyly to its mother's side, gazing out curiously from the stall with huge, liquid eyes. 'What a little darling!' she breathed. 'What's it called?'

Mr Quinn grinned down at her. 'Well, now, we ain't given him a name yet. Mebbe you'd better think of one, eh?'

Josey smiled in delight, and tipped her head on one side, regarding the young thing thoughtfully. 'Well, as his mother's called Saffron, it ought to be something a bit spicy too,' she mused. 'What about...Marjoram?'

'Marjoram?' Mr Quinn stroked his jaw, and looked down at the foal. 'Aye—Marjo—that'll do.' He picked up a bucket, and walked from the stall, patting her on the shoulder as he passed. 'Good lass.'

He went outside to fill the bucket, leaving her and Tom alone in the stables. Josey was stroking the foal, but still she was tensely aware of Tom. And as he stepped close to her, she jerked away quickly, every nerve-fibre in her body on edge.

He laughed in sardonic mockery. 'Relax,' he taunted. 'What do you think I'm going to do? Lay you down here in the hay and strip your clothes off?'

Somehow she managed to tilt up her chin. 'No,' she responded, her voice cool. 'But I hope you realise that your parents are quite sure we're having an affair. In fact, your mother thinks she can hear wedding bells!'

He lifted one dark eyebrow a fraction of an inch. 'Does she?' he enquired with faint amusement. 'Whatever gave you that impression?'

Josey felt her cheeks blush a deep pink—she could almost hate him when he was so dismissive of her concerns. 'She...she was so nice to me,' she stammered awkwardly. 'She told me to call her Phyllis.'

He shrugged his wide shoulders in a gesture of indifference. 'She's nice to everyone,' he demurred.

'Yes, but——'

The clang of the bucket warned of his father's return. Mr Quinn couldn't fail to notice the colour in her cheeks, and flicked them both a knowing glance, smiling contentedly. 'Well, we'd best be getting back to the house,' he said. 'Your mother won't want to wait lunch.'

It was through Helen, too, that Josey had met quite a few of the other young women in the district. And, ironically, it seemed that Vanessa had done her a favour, quite unintentionally. Apparently she had been gossiping bitchily about her to all and sundry, but since Vanessa herself was far from popular most of them were very ready to take her side.

In fact she didn't have a great deal of time to worry about Tom. Helen had recommended a local firm of builders, who due to a cancellation of some other work were able to start on the cottage right away. They had had a lot of experience in converting disused barns and windmills for the kind of second-home owners Tom so disliked, but she had managed to persuade them that she was looking for something much more simple and basic, and they were doing a very good job for her.

Now that her wrist was out of plaster, she had bought herself a nice little red Metro as a run-around, and when she wasn't out at the cottage she was shopping in Norwich or even Cambridge for curtain material and chair covers. And when she was at home the cosy kitchen was often filled with her new friends, their children playing on the floor with Pepper as they sat around the big scrubbed-pine table chatting and sipping coffee, and matching fabric swatches to paint samples.

'You know, I think this yellow would look pretty in the sitting-room,' remarked Maggie Hunter, smoothing out a flowered chintz. 'It's so nice and sunny-looking.'

'Which one's that?' asked Helen, reaching for it. 'Oh, yes—look, Josey, what do you think?'

'Yes, I was thinking of that one,' Josey agreed. 'And I thought this wallpaper would look nice with it.'

She had heard the Land Rover draw up outside, and there was no mistaking Jethro's sudden alertness, but she wasn't going even to glance up at the door as Tom came in—she was too busy with *interesting* things to even notice his presence.

'Here again, Helen?' he remarked teasingly to his sister-in-law as he tossed down his car keys. 'Are you sure you wouldn't like me to get Vi to make up a spare bed for you?'

Helen laughed. 'Don't be daft. Sit down, and I'll put the kettle on. We were just going to have another one, weren't we, girls?'

'Oh, not for me,' cried Maggie, glancing at her watch. 'I'd better be going. Harry, watch what you're doing,' she added as her small son almost crawled under Tom's feet, nearly making him lose his balance and step on a red plastic push-along truck. 'Sorry, Tom.'

'Oh, that's quite all right—don't mind me,' he assured her, playing the harassed male with wry amusement. Pepper, who adored him, was yapping excitedly at his ankles, tugging playfully at the laces of his boots, and he stooped to pick her up. 'Stop that,' he scolded, not in a voice that stood any chance of being taken notice of. 'You're a very naughty girl.'

Helen sighed. 'I suppose I'd better be going too,' she remarked. 'The Quinn Machine will be erupting from school at any moment, and I'd better be there to take it home or it's likely to wreak devastation on the whole village.' Thus Helen castigated her three adored children.

'Well, goodbye,' said Josey, rising to her feet to see them out. 'Mind how you go.'

'Come up tomorrow and I'll give you some cuttings from our lavender bush,' Maggie reminded her. 'It'll be lovely once you've got the garden going.'

'I will—thank you. Goodbye.' She waved them off, and then turned back reluctantly into the kitchen.

Tom was standing with his back to the empty fireplace, watching her. Silently she moved over to the table, and began to clear away the bags of shopping she had bought in Norwich earlier in the day. She could still feel him watching her, but she took no notice—she didn't want him to know just how much he affected her, even from that distance across the room.

'You seem to have made yourself very much at home here,' he remarked.

'Yes, I'm sorry, I wasn't expecting you so early. I meant to have taken it all upstairs before you came home.'

'I didn't mean that.' His voice had an odd note in it, forcing her to turn to look at his face. 'You seem to have made a lot of friends. Every time I come home the house is full of them.'

'I'm sorry.'

'Oh, you don't have to apologise.' He was becoming frustrated by her blank refusal to show him any emotion. 'I suppose it's nice for you, since you seem so dead set on staying here.'

'I am,' she responded coolly. 'But the cottage is nearly finished—I hope to be able to move by next

week, so you'll be able to have your house to yourself
again.'

He looked faintly surprised. 'Already? That was
quick. Will you . . . still come in and give me a hand
with the office work?'

'If you like.' She was surprised that he should ask
her, though she knew how much he needed it. 'A
couple of mornings a week should be enough to keep
it under control.'

'Good.' His voice was terse. 'We'll have to nego-
tiate some wages, of course.'

'Of course.' It was a struggle to suppress her anger.
She would have continued to do it for him for nothing,
as she had for the past four weeks, if he would only
once try to offer even the briefest 'thank you'.

She hurried upstairs to stow her shopping away. She
was going to miss this little room, with its low oak
beams and its view across the open Norfolk wheat-
fields. Of course the cottage was very nice, now that
the builders had almost finished their work on it, and
the garden had been cleared—Vi's husband had done
that for her; he had been forced into early retirement
from the farm he had worked on all his life, and was
glad to earn a little extra money by odd-jobbing
around the district.

But she would be on her own there. It was rather
strange, she reflected wryly, that after nine years she
could hardly remember what Colin looked like, and
yet in little more than a month she knew Tom with
an intimacy that would have alarmed him, had he
known of it.

She knew the way his dark hair curled around his
ears, knew about the row of scars on his left arm
where one of his former patients must have bitten him,

knew that he could always finish the Sunday crossword in half an hour unless the clues were obscure literary allusions—he read little, apart from the technical journals with which he conscientiously kept himself up to date. It seemed that that sated him for serious reading, and he preferred to relax by listening to music—often classical music, played loudly on a very expensive hi-fi system that was his only toy.

With a sigh she shook such wistful thoughts from her mind, and made herself resume the cool façade with which she had armed herself for the past few weeks before going downstairs. Tom was in his usual armchair, Pepper on his lap, trying to chew at the corner of the copy of the *Record* he was reading.

'Would you like a coffee?' she asked.

He barely glanced up. 'Yes, please.'

So they were back to normal again, after that brief attempt at conversation earlier. She went into the scullery and put the kettle on, gazing blankly out of the window at the passing life of the village—this was Vi's favourite vantage-point; she loved to stand here, where she could see and comment on everything that was going on.

A grey BMW drove slowly past. Josey blinked at it in surprise. Colin had one like that... Of course, it couldn't be him. Why would he drive all the way out here to see her himself? He would surely leave everything to his solicitors. But a few moments later the car came back, drawing to a halt right outside. Josey felt a stab of panic that almost stopped her heart. It *was* Colin. What on earth was he doing here?

Tom glanced up in surprise as she appeared in the doorway, her face ashen. 'Josey?' He rose swiftly to his feet, coming towards her. 'Josey, whatever's the matter...?' He turned as the doorbell rang, frowning. 'Who's that?'

'It's my husband.' Her voice emerged as a stricken whisper. All the newly found self-confidence that she had been building over the past few weeks was ebbing swiftly away—Colin could strip it down with just one sarcastic word. 'I'd...better let him in—if you don't mind?'

'Do you want me to stay?' he asked, his voice soft with concern.

She nodded, wanting to reach out and touch him, to draw on his strength. Suddenly the barriers that had been there between them for the past three weeks seemed to have melted away. His hands were on her shoulders, gently supportive, and a warmth seemed to flow from them as she lifted her misted eyes to his face.

But the doorbell rang again, sharp and impatient. 'You sit down,' said Tom grimly, steering her to a chair beside the kitchen table. 'I'll let him in.'

He strode over to the door, and pulled it open. His large frame almost entirely obscured what was beyond, but Josey caught a brief glimpse of Colin's startled face, looking up at the much larger man.

'Who the hell are you?' he demanded, betraying his uncertainty by his aggressive bluster.

'I live here,' responded Tom in laconic unconcern.

'You...? But...' For a moment Colin wavered, but then he spotted Josey, sitting at the kitchen table, and his lip curled into an unpleasant sneer. 'I see—how very cosy.'

'You'd better come in,' grated Tom, standing away from the doorway to let him pass.

Colin glanced up at him again, as if weighing up the risks, but after a moment he stepped inside, and Tom closed the door.

'Josey was just making some coffee,' he said. 'Would you like some? No, stay where you are, Josey—I'll finish it.' He withdrew pointedly to the scullery, leaving them alone together, but still close enough that they both knew that she still had his protection if she needed it.

But Colin had never been the sort to resort to violence. He cast a disparaging eye around the room. 'Very homely,' he commented with thinly veiled contempt. 'So this is where you've been living?'

'Yes.'

'With him?' He nodded his head back towards the scullery.

'Sort of,' she conceded.

'And what exactly is that supposed to mean?' he enquired sibilantly.

She turned her eyes away from him, wishing she could suppress the blush of pink that was rising to her cheeks. 'It's...not what you think,' she forced out.

'No?' He sounded faintly amused. 'Well, that's reassuring. It wouldn't do my ego a great deal of good to know that you'd supplanted me with the local ploughboy.'

'As a matter of fact,' she parried, anger giving her the courage to face him, 'he's a veterinary surgeon. And he's worth a hundred of you.'

'Oh, really?' He was trying to maintain his mocking pose, but Josey knew him well enough to know that she had managed to knock him slightly off balance.

At that moment Tom came back into the room, carrying the coffee-cups, which he set down on the table, and sat down himself at the far end, facing Colin, as Josey sat in the middle. Colin flickered him a nervous glance, not quite sure what part he intended to play in these proceedings—Tom's face, as usual, gave nothing away.

'Besides,' Josey pointed out, anxious to turn the conversation before it became too awkward, 'if I remember correctly it was *you* who had supplanted *me*. How is Paula?'

The slight twitch at the corner of Colin's mouth betrayed his tension. 'She's very well, thank you. She sends her regards.'

'How very sweet of her,' Josey returned acidly. 'Please send her my heartfelt sympathy. Have you set the date for the wedding yet?'

'Of course we haven't—we can't do that until the divorce is settled.' Colin was impatient, but clearly disconcerted at finding her in such a belligerent frame of mind. 'As a matter of fact, that's why I'm here.'

'I thought it might be.' Butter wouldn't have melted in her mouth.

'We have to discuss this settlement.' He had set his briefcase down on the floor, and now he bent to open it, taking out a sheaf of papers. As he turned away, Josey's eyes flickered automatically towards Tom, and found that his had turned towards her, offering a reassurance that she could draw on to sustain her through this ordeal.

'I really don't think we should discuss it,' she said to Colin. 'I'd prefer to leave it all in the hands of my solicitor.'

'Bah—solicitors!' expostulated Colin, changing his tactics abruptly and turning on his most charming smile. 'If you leave it all to them they have you at each other's throats, while they pocket a nice fat fee. I mean, just look at this.' He tossed down the papers on the table with a gesture of contempt. 'Have you any idea what he's demanding on your behalf? It's ludicrous.'

'He's simply acting on my instructions,' she responded, totally cool.

'Oh, come on.' He tried a laugh. 'You can't be serious. This is half my assets you're asking for!'

'Exactly half, I believe,' she agreed cordially. 'I think that's what I'm entitled to.'

'*Entitled* to?' He had soon abandoned the pretence of pleasantry. 'And what for, exactly? What can you possibly think you've done to earn all that?'

'I helped you start up the business,' she reminded him, her voice steady, though inside she was starting to shake. 'You made me a director...'

He made a dismissive gesture with his hand. 'That was just a matter of formality. All you ever had to do was sign a few papers now and then.'

'Nevertheless, I am entitled to my share. And as well as that, I took care of the house for you for nine years. I organised dinner parties for your friends...'

'Quite the little geisha,' he sneered. 'Are you going to charge for *all* the services you provided? Because, quite frankly, some of them weren't worth very much, as I recall. I'd have got more satisfaction out of a sack of potatoes.'

Unerring as usual, he had struck right on her raw nerve, and Josey could feel herself crumbling. She couldn't even bring herself to look in Tom's direction. All she wanted to do was run away and hide. She couldn't fight Colin—she had never been able to fight him.

The glint of triumph was in Colin's eyes. 'I think we can come to some sort of compromise,' he suggested, at his most patronising. 'I've drawn up a list of—— Damn you! You little rat,' he broke off abruptly. 'Leave that alone!'

Unnoticed while they were talking, little Pepper had settled down beside his briefcase, and was contentedly chewing on one leather corner, making a nice meal of it with her sharp little teeth. He kicked out at her viciously, and with a squeal of alarm she darted out of his way and ran for cover behind Josey's chair.

Josey scooped her up in her arms. 'Don't you *dare* kick my dog!' she flared at him tearfully, hugging the puppy close for reassurance.

Colin laughed. '*Your* dog?' he scorned. 'What are you doing with a dog? You can't even look after yourself. Look at you, getting hysterical as usual, when I'm just trying to hold a rational discussion——'

'I think that's enough.' Tom's quiet voice startled them both—he had been sitting there so silent; watchful, but taking no part in the conversation. Now he rose to his feet, and came round to take Josey gently by the shoulders. 'Why don't you just take Pepper upstairs for a few minutes, out of the way?'

She stared up at him uncertainly. She didn't want to leave the two men alone, afraid that Colin would find some sneaky way to turn Tom against her. But she knew she needed a few minutes to calm herself down. And besides, when he looked at her like that, she found it impossible to argue with him. So without another word she carried Pepper up the stairs to her bedroom.

The pup was looking decidedly anxious as Josey settled her in her own little basket, beside her bed. She tickled her ear, laughing softly. 'You did well there, anyway, sweetheart,' she murmured to her proudly. 'You've ruined his precious briefcase.'

The puppy stuck out her little pink tongue, enthusiastically licking her hand.

Suddenly there was a sound from below—a scuffle, and a thud. Startled, Josey ran to the top of the stairs, in time to see Colin picking himself up gingerly from the kitchen floor. 'That was assault!' he threatened furiously, though backing warily out of Tom's way. 'I'll get the police on to you.'

'I don't think so,' responded Tom with a sardonic smile. 'We stick together around here. If I were you I'd clear off back to London. And you'd better not try bullying Josey any more—you'll have to come past me first.'

Colin glanced up, and saw her on the stairs. He tried a sarcastic laugh, keeping the table safely between himself and Tom. 'Oh, you can keep the physical stuff, ploughboy,' he sneered. 'It won't do you much good in court. I'll contest this, you know— I'll cross-petition. I wonder what the judge will make of this little love-nest?'

Josey looked down at him, realising with a sudden jolt of surprise that he was really a very small, blustering little man. 'By all means,' she responded to him coolly. 'Of course, you realise how much time that will take? And if Paula wants to be married before the baby's due...'

She knew by the expression on his face that she had struck a raw nerve. 'Damn you!' he spluttered. 'You've turned into a right calculating little bitch, you know that?' He threw his papers into his wounded briefcase, tucking it under his arm. 'You're welcome to her,' he threw at Tom, and then turned with as much dignity as he could muster and stalked out of the house.

Josey was laughing as she came down the rest of the stairs into Tom's arms. 'Why did you hit him?' she asked, a little surprised to find how delighted she was.

'He tried to hit me first,' Tom explained, smiling down at her. 'Which was a little foolish of him. I may not have been in a fight since I was at school, but when you spend your life conducting examinations of an intimate and personal nature on a variety of large farm animals you maintain pretty swift reflexes.'

She gurgled with merriment, laying her forehead against his wide chest, and he stroked his hand down over her hair.

'You *don't* love him any more, do you?' he asked softly.

'No.' She shook her head, not looking at him—she wasn't quite ready to face the consequences of that yet. 'I haven't loved him for a long time. In fact . . . I wonder if I ever did. He . . . sort of rushed me, and I didn't really have time to think.'

He put his hand beneath her chin, lifting her face, and it seemed the most natural thing in the world as their mouths came together in a sweet, lingering kiss. Josey closed her eyes, aching with the joy of this moment that she had waited for through three lean, hungry weeks.

Passion deepened swiftly, like a river in flood. His arms wrapped around her, and she clung to him, too overcome with loving him to speak the words aloud. He was moulding her to him, so close that she couldn't help but feel the powerful tension of male arousal in him. And for one wild, glorious moment her own responses flamed in answer...

But then suddenly came panic, as she remembered what had happened before. What if she couldn't please him? What if he was disappointed in her, as Colin had been? Desperately she tried to recapture her previous wanton abandon, but Tom was far too wise not to know that she was faking it. He lifted his head, and looked down enquiringly into her eyes.

'What is it?' he asked softly. His hand moved to gently caress her breast. 'Don't be frightened, Josey. All I want to do is make love to you. I won't hurt you.'

'No.' It was almost a sob, and she lowered her head, resisting his attempts to make her lift it again to look up at him. 'I'm sorry...'

'Hey... Don't be sorry. It's no problem.' He held her tenderly close, stroking her hair, so soothing, slowly stilling the trembling that had racked her body. 'Was it him?' he asked, his voice rough-edged. 'Was he...violent? Did he used to hit you?'

'Oh, no.' She shook her head quickly. 'It... it was me. I never...I could never...enjoy it.' The tears were spilling over. 'I'm frigid.'

He was silent for a moment, and then he began to laugh, incredulously. 'Are you kidding?' he protested. 'You're not frigid. You just need to be made love to properly.' He brushed his thumb lightly across her trembling lips. 'All it takes is a little time,' he murmured, his voice low and husky. 'You don't have to worry—there's no hurry. We'll take it one step at a time—nothing will happen until you're sure you're ready for it. Besides, you're still a married woman,' he added, a gleam of devilish promise in his eyes. 'I really think we ought to wait until your divorce comes through.'

She gazed up at him in wide-eyed apprehension. He had spoken with an intent that she knew absolutely would not be deflected. He wanted her, and he wanted her to respond to him as a woman—and she knew that he could make it happen.

But he hadn't said a word about love.

CHAPTER EIGHT

ONE step at a time.

The cottage was finished, and Josey had moved into it, amid considerable excitement from all her new friends, who had come to help her, and had decked the place out with flowers, and painted a huge 'welcome' sign on a sheet hung above the front door.

It was the first time she had ever lived alone, and it had been a big step. But it was impossible to be lonely. She still came down into the village almost every day—she had found that her secretarial skills were very much in demand. The vicar had roped her in to deal with the accounts for the various little groups who used the church hall, and several of the local farmers were very glad of her help with their EC paperwork. And three mornings a week she still worked for Tom.

Now that she was no longer living in his house, their relationship was able to follow a more normal pattern. He had even taken her out—twice to dinner in Norwich, and once to the theatre in Cambridge. And slowly, one step at a time, he had led her to accept more and more of his caresses. He had said that they would wait until she was divorced, and he had kept his word—but only just. Her cheeks flamed scarlet at the thought of just how close they had come to the brink.

And now there was an official brown envelope on the mat. Josey stood looking down at it, her mouth dry. The solicitor had told her that she didn't need to attend the court for the divorce hearing—he would notify her as soon as the decree nisi was granted. Her hand was shaking as she picked up the envelope, and tore it open.

The words on the paper seemed to swim before her eyes, and it took a moment to focus clearly. She had hardly dared to hope that it could all go through so smoothly, but Colin had decided not to contest the financial settlement after all, and, with no children of the marriage to be considered, it had been more or less a routine matter.

So—she was no longer married. Nine years of her life, quietly obliterated—and all she felt was relief. Folding the letter carefully, she slipped it into her handbag, and called to Pepper.

The little dog came scampering out from the kitchen, her eyes bright with excitement. She had had her final injections now, and so was allowed out. She loved nothing better than a long rambling walk along the river-bank, barking at the little brown bittern chicks scudding among the reeds, chasing dragonflies and getting her paws muddy.

Josey picked her up, laughing as she wriggled and tried to lick her ear. 'No, we're not going for a walk yet,' she told her. 'It's Friday, and I've got to go down and do Tom's accounts for him. But you can play in the kitchen with Jethro.'

She snapped on Pepper's smart red leather lead, and then fastened the safety harness that would hold her into her seatbelt, and carried her out to the car. It had been a lovely summer, golden days of sunshine following each other without a break; the sky was the most incredible blue, and seemed to go on for ever.

Josey had come to love the wide Norfolk landscape—almost, but never quite, flat. The feeling of spaciousness, after so many years of being hemmed in by city buildings, gave her a sense of freedom, of being able to really breathe for the first time in many years.

The whole village was in a state of high excitement. Tomorrow was Vanney Hal, a traditional festival that took place in the village every year on the Bank Holiday weekend. Its roots were lost in the mists of time, and it had become something of a tourist attraction, but she could sense an underlying seriousness in the way people went about the preparations, as if some remnant of the pagan spirit still lingered somewhere deep in the collective unconscious.

But her mind wasn't on that today. There was a little knot of anticipation tightening in the pit of her stomach as she approached the veterinary surgery. But the Land Rover wasn't in its place—Tom was out, then. Vi was in the kitchen, listening to her favourite radio phone-in programme as she black-leaded the fire-grate.

'Tch—these people that ring up,' she grumbled, rising heavily to her feet. 'I don't know how they can be so daft. Why don't I put the kettle on, and we can have a nice cup of tea?'

'I'll do it,' offered Josey, putting Pepper down to romp with Jethro.

It was really rather a relief that Tom wasn't in. She needed a little more time to work out how she was going to tell him about the contents of that brown envelope. Once she told him she had the decree . . . It wasn't exactly that she was afraid any more—how could she be afraid, when she loved him so much? It was just that . . . it was a very big step.

She drank her tea at the kitchen table with Vi, and then went through to the office. It had taken her several weeks to put all of Tom's records and accounts on to the computer, but the task was finished now. He had had to admit that she had been right about the improved speed and efficiency of the system—though he hadn't actually got around to letting her teach him how to use it yet, always claiming that he didn't have the time.

And it had taken her some time to learn his personal system for sending out bills. There were some farmers that he always billed promptly, sending out crisp reminders when they failed to pay; others he left on file until he saw them in the village pub on market day, when he would come home with a bundle of dirty old fivers in his pocket, and as often as not a note scribbled on the back of a beer-mat reminding him of who had given him what. Others again paid in kind—a side of lamb for the freezer, or a sack of potatoes, or a service to the Land Rover—not always when it needed one. And one or two of the old folks simply paid what they had been paying for thirty or forty years for attention to their much-loved companions.

The dogs, tired of their game, came in to lie at her feet as she worked, and the morning ticked away slowly, with no sign of Tom. It was hard to concentrate on what she was doing—her mind kept turning round and round, thinking of what she would say to him when he came in. But always the thought of what would happen next would make her heart begin to

flutter and her mouth go dry, and for her sanity's sake
she would have to try to think of something else.

Vi had finished her chores and left, just popping
her head round the door to say goodbye, before she
finally heard the familiar sound of the Land Rover's
engine. The dogs leapt up, darting out to the kitchen
to bark at the door, and Josey waited, tense, for him
to come to her.

He appeared in the office doorway, leaning casually
against it, smiling at her. That broad-shouldered,
masculine frame that had so impressed her the very
first time she had seen him still had the power to make
her feel weak—more so now, because there were so
many vivid memories of how it felt to be held in those
strong arms. And that smile was so familiar now, but
no less devastating in its impact.

'Hello,' she greeted him, trying to keep her voice
light. 'I've almost finished here. Would you like a cup
of coffee?'

'That sounds like a very good idea,' he agreed,
letting his eyes drift down lingeringly over all her
slender curves as she rose to her feet. She felt a warm
blush spread through her, but it was a delicious sensation—that look told her just how much he wanted
her. And as she stepped forward to pass him, he
blocked her, drawing her firmly into his arms. 'But
how about a kiss first?' he demanded huskily.

His mouth at once claimed hers in a kiss that was
pure sensuality, his lips moving intoxicatingly over
hers, his tongue plundering into the sweetest depths
in a reminder, as if she needed one, of how total his
possession would be when the time came.

If he knew the letter had arrived . . . A nervous little
shiver ran through her at the thought. She couldn't

tell him, not yet—she needed just a little more time. And besides, when he was kissing her like this . . .

He had pushed her gently back against the desk, so that her body was curved every inch against his hard length, and his hand had moved to the tiny buttons down the front of her cotton blouse, unfastening them one by one. She held her breath, aching with the anticipation of his touch.

Since he had started this long, slow seduction she had spent a small fortune on the most beautiful underwear, delicate bras of lace and silk, that fastened at the front. Her curves were just a little fuller now, and his smouldering gaze let her know how much he admired the creamy swell of her breasts, tightly encased in their dainty lace cups. Once she would have been shy of letting him look at her like this, but now she felt only a kind of pride in her own femininity, a joy in her sexuality.

Tom smiled slowly, letting the tip of one finger trail down from her throat, until he found the tiny hook fastening nestling in the soft valley between her breasts. 'Ah,' he murmured in soft satisfaction. 'You're wearing this one today. My favourite—so easy to undo.'

The scrap of fabric fell away, uncovering the nakedness of her ripe breasts, the soft rose nipples already taut as they awaited the magic of his caress, and he laughed in gentle mockery. 'And this is the woman who thought she was frigid,' he teased, drawing her back into his arms, his kiss deep and tender, his hands firm and possessive on her breasts.

He was ruthless, but not cruel, tormenting her with a pleasure that had her whimpering into his shoulder as he rolled the swollen, tender nipples beneath his palms, pinching at them teasingly, reducing her to a state of helpless abandon.

He had lifted her on to the edge of the desk, wrapping her legs around his body. She felt his hand lift the hem of her light cotton skirt, felt the brush of his fingers up over the slender length of her thighs as he drew her close against him, making her devastatingly aware of the hard tension of male arousal in him.

His hot mouth was tracing a path of fire down the long, vulnerable curve of her throat to dwell in the sensitive hollows, his sinuous tongue tracing tiny circles over her fevered skin. They were breathing together, each breath deep and ragged, as velvet cloaks of darkness wrapped around them, shutting out all else but their knowledge of each other.

His shirt was a frustrating annoyance, and she snatched impatiently at the buttons, unfastening them quickly so she could wrap her arms around his warm, powerful body, rest her cheek against that hard chest, where the rough smattering of dark curls tickled her cheek, and she could feel the power of his heartbeat vibrating through her.

'I love you, Tom,' she whispered desperately, just loud enough so that he could hear if he wanted to. But he didn't answer her—he never did.

He lifted her back, and her head swam dizzily; she knew what he was going to do to her—he had done this before—and she whimpered in anticipation. He laughed huskily, teasing her. 'You like this, don't you?' he murmured. 'You always want more.'

It was true—what sort of wanton creature had she become that she could be so hungry for such caresses? She couldn't even pardon herself with the excuse that he loved her—though he was caring and tender, he had made no pretence of that.

But as his head bent over one ripe, aching breast, all rational thought evaporated clean away. His kisses were lighter than the wings of the swallowtail butterfly that danced among the marsh thistles, dusting paths of fire around and over the warm roundness, circling closer and tantalisingly closer to the hardened, tender peaks.

She was cracking, begging him in sobbing whispers, moving to offer him the dainty, succulent fruits, but he evaded her, tormenting her with frustration until he was good and ready. And then his soft, rasping tongue lapped in a swirling curve around one taut pink nipple, grazing it gently with his strong teeth, nibbling it between his lips, and at last taking it deep into his mouth to suckle with a pulsing rhythm that almost drove her out of her mind.

He paused only to offer the same sweet torment to the other breast, his expert fingers caressing the first to maintain it in a state of sweet sensitivity. She was melting, her spine turning to liquid, and he laid her back gently across the desk, lifting the hem of her skirt back over her thighs.

Suddenly she was shy. Her legs were bare, and she was wearing only the daintiest pair of white lace briefs, which did little to conceal the soft downy crest of curls beneath. She tensed, longing to curl up away from him, afraid of what he might do.

But his touch was so smooth and light, stroking up over her silken skin, coaxing her to relax. 'Shhh—it's all right,' he whispered persuasively. 'I'm not going to do anything.'

Just those leisurely, soothing strokes and soft kisses, slowly winning her trust, as he had won it step by step from the beginning. She knew that he was accustoming her to his touch, as if she were a frightened animal, until she was ready to let him move on, and already she was wondering, with a quivering apprehension, what that next step would be.

But then abruptly he stopped, pulling her skirt down and lifting her into his arms. 'There—I think that's enough for now,' he murmured, holding her against him.

She clung to him, wishing he hadn't stopped. It was always like that—he always seemed to know the exact moment that would leave her wanting just a little bit more. His chest was hard and warm against her breasts, the rough smattering of hair rasping over her tender nipples, and she deliberately crushed herself against him, almost wanting to incite him beyond the bounds of that iron self-control.

He laughed, knowing exactly what she was doing, and put his hand into her hair, gently tugging back her head. 'Careful,' he warned, his eyes still smouldering with the memory of what they had been doing. 'You're walking a very fine line.'

She hesitated, her breath caught up on a moment of uncertainty. Should she tell him now about the letter? Then he would scoop her up in his arms, and carry her through to his bedroom... But as she opened her mouth to speak, her courage failed her. Tomorrow—she would tell him tomorrow.

He had lifted one dark eyebrow, enquiring what she had been going to say, and her mind sought swiftly for the first words she could think of. 'I'll ... put the kettle on,' was what came out.

He laughed, and, taking the fastening of her bra, he clipped it neatly together for her. 'All right,' he said, the reluctance in his voice telling her that he had been hoping that she was going to relent. 'But it's not going to be much longer, Josey. I know I said we'd wait until your divorce came through...'

She lowered her eyes, on the pretext of fastening her buttons. 'Oh, it shouldn't be much longer now,' she conceded a little breathlessly. 'Any day, in fact.'

She heard him draw in his breath as he fought that battle within himself for the supremacy of his will, and then he stepped back from her, buttoning his own shirt. 'You'd better go and make that coffee,' he said. 'I can survive on cold showers a little longer.'

He followed her into the kitchen, sitting on the edge of the big table to read his post as she went through to the scullery to put the kettle on. 'Are you coming down to Vanney Hal tomorrow?' she asked him, trying to take the conversation into lighter channels.

'Of course—I wouldn't miss it. I've fixed up with Paul Leyton to cover for me.'

There was a small, cracked piece of mirror propped up on the window-sill, and Josey caught a glimpse of her own reflection in it. How different she looked now from when she had first arrived! She had put on weight, just a little, enough to take the gaunt hollows from her cheeks, and her colour now was a healthy cream instead of that awful pallor. Her hair had bounce and shine, and her eyes... now that the deadening effect of the sleeping pills she had taken for so long had worn off, they had a sparkle, a warmth in them. Being in the country was doing her good—or was it being in love?

'I'm dying to find out what it's all about,' she re-marked as she brought the two mugs in from the scullery. 'I've heard all sorts of little bits, but no one will really tell me the whole thing. What does Vanney Hal mean?'

He laughed, a low husky laugh that hinted at all sorts of intriguing secrets. 'Ah, well "Vanney" is probably a corruption of *Vanir*,' he told her, linking his arms loosely around her waist. 'The old Norse fer-tility gods of earth and sea.'

'Fertility gods?' There was a choke in her voice, and a flame in her cheeks.

'Mmm.' He drew her a little closer against him, sliding his hands down over the smooth curve of her derrière to nestle her intimately between his thighs. 'Of course, the meaning's all forgotten now—most of it's just for the tourists. But even so, on the night of Vanney Hal, out here on the wild marshes...'

The wicked glint in his eyes made her laugh, and try to wriggle away from him, but he wouldn't let her go, clearly enjoying the squirming of her body against his. The fever inside her was rising again, making her breathless...

The sound of the latch on the door jerked them apart as Sandra walked in. The look of shock and hurt on her face betrayed the fact that she had guessed what had been going on, but she bravely tried to force a smile. 'Oh... Hello, Josey. Hello... Tom.'

At least she was making the effort, Josey accorded, feeling almost sorry for her, 'Hello, Sandra,' she res-ponded, smiling back.

But Tom had no such forbearance. 'Hello, Sandra,' he grated, impatience barely restrained. 'There are two cats in for spaying this afternoon. Would you like to start getting them ready before Hugh gets here? Please,' he added as an afterthought.

'OK, Tom.' She gave him a swift, devoted look, and withdrew.

Josey moved away from him as Sandra went through to the clinic. He slanted her a wry look. 'Well, at least you have to admit I'm civil to her now,' he pointed out, reading her thoughts.

'Yes . . .' she conceded. 'But I wish she hadn't seen . . . us. She gets so jealous, and it isn't really fair on her.'

'It's a good job she didn't come in ten minutes earlier,' he reminded her teasingly. 'Anyway, it's time she grew up, and found herself a proper boyfriend. You can't say I've ever given her the least encouragement.' He came up behind her again, wrapping his arms around her, nibbling at her ear. 'I was hoping she'd get the message while you were still here, but it doesn't look as if she's going to.'

Josey heard his words, and grew very still. 'What do you mean, "while I'm still here"?' she queried, her voice quiet and controlled.

He smiled wryly, and moved away from her, not answering her question. But she knew what he had meant. He still didn't believe that she was going to stay. Was that why he wouldn't allow their relationship to be anything more than sexual? Would he *ever* allow himself to trust her enough to love her?

No one was prepared to rely solely on the BBC weather report when it had promised a sunny day—for Vanney Hal, much more reliable portents were needed. Had three crows been sighted on one branch? Were the cows lying down or standing up? Was old Walter's shrapnel wound—gained on the Somme, as he never tired of telling anyone who would buy him a pint in the Barley Mow and sit still long enough to listen— giving him gyp?

Whatever, although the day had begun with some threatening cloud, by mid-morning it had cleared, and the sun was warm and bright. Crowds had already gathered on the village green by the time Josey arrived—it seemed as if everyone in the district was there, as well as the noticeable flocks of tourists, everyone in their brightest summer clothes.

The green was a rough triangle, with the church at the top end, and in front of it the stone cross of the war memorial. A single oak tree rose in the middle— once there had been three elms, too, but now they were only stumps, used for seats. The houses, mostly of traditional brick and flint like Tom's, straggled around it with no regard for the neatness of town-planning.

'Josey!' Helen, spotting her as she wandered through the crowds, called out, waving vigorously. 'Over here—we've saved you a space.'

All the family was there—the three children, and Tom's parents, and Hugh too. They had spread a large blanket on the ground, like many of the other family groups, staking out a territory with the best view of the entertainments, and were enjoying a picnic lunch.

And Tom was sitting with them. Josey hesitated, suddenly a little uncertain. Though she knew that their relationship was no secret, up to now they hadn't really been seen together by most of the villagers. If she joined them now, it would be making it public—and she wasn't at all sure that that was what Tom wanted.

Pepper, however, had no such inhibitions. Instantly recognising her favourite person, she yapped excitedly, scrabbling as close to him as her head would allow, trying to lick his face. He laughed, tickling her in just the right spot behind her ears to reduce her to a state of besotted adoration. Then he smiled up at Josey.

'Come and sit down,' he invited casually, taking her hand and drawing her down on to the rug, nestling her between his legs and wrapping his arms around her waist from behind, propping his chin on her shoulder. 'Sara, go and tell your daddy to fetch another half for Josey.'

'Have a sandwich,' invited Helen, holding out a Tupperware box. 'There's egg and cress, and cheese and cress, or there's salmon in the other one if you'd prefer it.'

'Thank you,' responded Josey with a happy smile as Phyllis passed her a paper plate to put the sandwiches on. Her heart was dancing; Tom had acknowledged their relationship, so simply, so naturally, in front of everyone—why had she ever doubted it? And his family had always made her feel so welcome—it was such a simple thing, to be part of a big family group like this, but it was something she had never really known.

Donald came out of the pub with a large tray of drinks, and Josey found herself with a half-pint glass in her hand. She regarded it with a shade of apprehension. She didn't usually drink beer—just maybe the odd half of lager now and then. And this was powerful stuff—locally brewed, with a rich, earthy flavour, but sipping it she found it was cool and very welcome on the throat.

So this was what Vanney Hal was all about, she mused, gazing around. Lots of the young girls were dressed in white, and had garlands of leaves and wild flowers in their hair, and most of the small children were carrying little round wicker baskets, filled with summer fruits—already many chubby faces were liberally smeared with raspberry juice.

A group of morris dancers were performing, their white shirts and trousers freshly laundered, the bells at their knees and ankles jangling as they wove their intricate steps, as the fiddler played a lively jig. Pepper thought it all looked rather fun, and wanted to join in, straining at the end of her leash and barking loudly.

'Hey, come on, that's enough,' laughed Josey, hauling her up on to her lap. 'If you're going to get over-excited you'll have to go back indoors by yourself.'

'Can we play with her?' pleaded Hugh, Helen's elder boy, eagerly.

Josey smiled. 'All right. But don't let her run loose—heaven knows where she'd get to in this crowd!'

She nestled back against Tom, laughing as he leaned over her shoulder to take a bite out of her sandwich. Across on the far side of the green, Sandra had spotted them, but instead of the usual look of misery she smiled and waved cheerfully. She was looking remarkably pretty today, Josey reflected, in a swirling white frock, her hair caught back from her face—and Bill Whickam's eldest lad was making very sure that no other young men paid her too much attention.

It seemed incredible, she reflected, that she had been here only three months. She felt as if she had lived here all her life. Looking around the crowd, she rec-

ognised nearly all the faces—except for the tourists,
of course—and lots of people were stopping to chat.

'Uh-oh,' warned Helen softly. 'Here comes
Vanessa!'

The lady of the manor was strolling arm in arm
with her husband, in a display of warm affection that
Josey suspected was mainly for public consumption.
She paused as she came level with them. 'Why,
Josey—Tom. Hello,' she greeted them, her smile pure
saccharin. 'How lovely to see you.'

Josey nodded a response, aware of Tom's possessive arm around her waist.

'Oh, is that the little puppy you rescued?' cooed
Vanessa, hunkering down beside the children. 'Isn't
he sweet? What have you called him?'

'*She's* called Pepper,' Josey responded with a dry
smile. The little dog, totally undiscriminating, had
accepted this new member of her fan club happily,
and was licking Vanessa's hand with all her usual
enthusiasm.

In fact Pepper was very much the centre of attention—everyone had heard about her, but this was
the first time she had been out in the village. She was
delighted that so many people had come along *just*
to see her. 'She'd be signing autographs if she could,'
murmured Tom with a quirk of humour.

With a twinge of embarrassment, Josey realised how
many people were watching them, smiling in indulgent approval. She knew what they were all
thinking. Although she had gained some measure of
acceptance in the village—in spite of the circumstance
of having been seen to be living with Tom for the first
few weeks—she knew that convention still largely
ruled. It would be expected that she and Tom would,

in the normal course of events, get engaged, and eventually get married.

But that didn't seem very likely to happen—Tom didn't seem at all willing to make that kind of commitment. Well, at least he had been honest about it, she acknowledged wryly. She could make up her own mind, with her eyes wide open, whether she was prepared to settle for just an affair.

The letter from the solicitor was still in her handbag. Sooner or later, of course, she was going to have to tell him about it. And then... Well, the assumption had been made, and conceded, that, once her divorce had come through, they would become lovers.

Of course, there was still time to change her mind. She could back off, tell him she wasn't ready... But she couldn't expect him to wait around for ever—there were far too many other young women more than eager to take her place. She was going to have to decide, one way or the other. And she was going to have to decide soon.

CHAPTER NINE

THE MORRIS dancing was lively and fun; several groups gave displays, and then there was folk-singing, and a performance by a ceilidh band down from Glasgow. And as the evening began to draw in, turning the sky to a rich cobalt-blue, there was a kind of folk-play.

Lit by the orange glow of flickering torches, there was something strangely surreal about the scene. All the roles, male and female, were played by men from the village. The characters were all traditional, dressed in strange and colourful costumes; each one that appeared was instantly recognised by the audience, and cheered or hissed like characters in a pantomime.

Josey watched in fascination, trying to guess who was playing the parts from the sound of their voices. 'That's Donald, isn't it?' she whispered to Tom in surprise as Slasher, a character in a red coat and knee-britches, introduced himself.

He nodded. 'Dad used to play it, but he's getting a bit old for it now, so it's passed to Donald. It'll be young Hugh's turn next. Some of the roles have been in the same family for generations.'

'What happens if there's no one to follow on?'

'Then another family takes over,' he told her. 'It has to be someone born in the village—the nearest kin, if possible. But it doesn't happen very often— even people who moved away years ago still come back to take part.'

'But eventually, I suppose, when they get too old, and their sons haven't been born in the village, the rules will have to change?'

'I suppose so,' he conceded. 'But it'll be a shame.'

'Maybe they'll even have to let the women take part,' she suggested with a giggle.

He rolled his eyes in teasing horror. 'Heaven forbid!'

The ending of the play marked a break in the festivities, a time for children to be taken protestingly home to bed. Josey took Pepper back to the cottage, to feed her and settle her in her basket for the night, while Tom went back to the surgery to check with his locum that everything was all right. They met up again outside the Barley Mow, where everyone was gathering, and as the ale flowed freely the atmosphere was getting noisier by the minute.

Around ten o'clock, as if by some unspoken signal, a ragged procession began to form up along the side of the village green, led by the fiddler and the antler-headed mummer from the play. In the darkness, the flickering shadows on orange-lit faces added to the growing air of expectation.

'What happens now?' Josey asked Tom quietly.

'Now we dance the Fandy all round the village,' he told her. 'And then we go down to meet Vanney Hal.'

'*Meet* it?' she repeated, puzzled. 'What do you mean?'

He slanted her a mysterious smile. 'You'll see.'

The procession had started off, singing a kind of doggerel song as they wound their way up through the village. Josey found that it wasn't really necessary to know the words of the song, or the steps of the dance. She just joined in, as they circled around the top of the village, in between the houses, and then along the narrow lane beside Breck's Coppice, down to Bill Whickham's bottom field.

A great bonfire had been lit, the hot flames leaping up into the night sky. Three times the chanting procession danced around it, forming a large circle, before finally stopping as everyone struggled to recover their breath. Then the mummer stepped forward, striking the ground with his thick staff, and instantly silence fell.

It was the weirdest thing. There was a palpable tension in the air, and Josey could almost imagine that she really was going to see the apparition of the ancient Norse god. Maybe she had had too much of that powerful ale! And then the mummer recited some strange lines, accompanied by a hollow drum sound from the darkness beyond. And then, holding up the thick staff he had been holding in his hand, he held one end of it into the bonfire. It kindled, and began to burn.

Some of the men had begun to move forward, forming a smaller circle around the mummer and his flaming staff. Little spats, conducted in hushed voices, were breaking out between husbands and wives— 'You're *not* joining in. Please, you promised last year...'

Josey felt a sudden flutter of apprehension. What was going on? Someone called, 'Come on, Tom,' and Josey grabbed instinctively at his arm, trying to hold him back, wanting to beg him not to go. But she sensed that this was something older and stronger than modern reason; this was a pagan rite, steeped in superstition, and it wasn't for her to interfere.

Tom laughed down into her panic-stricken eyes. 'It's all right,' he murmured softly. 'I won't get hurt.' His mouth came down on hers in a deep, fierce kiss, hotter than the flames of the bonfire, and she clung to him, not believing his assurance.

A cold chill ran over her as he let her go, and went to take his place in the circle. Helen took her arm, drawing her back with the other women, and smiled reassuringly. 'Don't worry,' she murmured. 'None of them ever really hurts himself. It's just a little boys' game, really.'

But she didn't sound entirely relaxed herself, and looking at the strained, anxious faces around her Josey felt far from comforted.

The chanting had begun again, slow and hypnotic, almost as if it came out of the ground itself. Josey felt as if she was being dragged back through a time-warp, into some medieval etching. The flickering flames of the bonfire lighting the scene only added to the illusion.

The mummer's staff was aflame down three-quarters of its length now, and carefully he passed it to one of the men. It was crackling and snapping like an angry demon, spitting curses, as it was passed on, moving slowly around the circle.

Josey watched in a mixture of horror and fascination, hardly able to breathe. 'What's it all about?' she whispered to Helen.

'The staff is the spirit of Vanney Hal. It's made of ash-wood, bound with rags soaked in tar, all but the bottom few inches. As it's passed around, each man must take it, or fall out of the circle. It mustn't be dropped—that would bring terrible bad luck to the

whole village. The winner is the last one left holding
it.'

'But what's the point?' persisted Josey, watching
anxiously as the staff, now alight down its full length,
passed safely through Tom's hands for the second
time.

Helen laughed softly. 'There's no point, really. It's
just one of those ancient customs that no one really
understands any more, like the play. But it would be
a shame to let it die out, and not pass it on to our
children.'

'Doesn't anyone ever get burned?'

'Not badly.'

Helen's prosaic attitude did a little to comfort her,
but not much. Some of the men were beginning to
drop out now—some dragged back by worried wives
or mothers—but Tom was still there. The staff had
made another complete circuit, and was burning
fiercely. More men stepped back, rather than take it—
but not Tom.

The chanting was growing steadily faster, and Josey
could feel her heartbeat accelerating with it. Donald
had dropped out of the circle, smiling wryly, and now
there were only four left. One of them hesitated for
a split second as it came to his turn, and lost his nerve.
Three.

Josey wanted to scream. It was crazy—why were
they doing this? In the light of the flames each face
was set with a concentration so intense that they
seemed aware of nothing else. She sensed that that
concentration must not be allowed to waver for even
so much as an instant...

The staff passed to Tom, and he held it out to the
next man. But he hesitated, and then shook his head,

refusing to take it. A breath of expectation rippled through the ring of watchers. The last man put out his hand . . . and drew it back.

With a loud cheer, the men surged forward, lifting Tom high on their shoulders as he held the staff triumphantly aloft. It was then that Josey began to understand. Earth, water, wind and fire; the four elements—and the most dangerous of these was fire. And mastery over fire was the ultimate proof of mastery over nature—to show that you could control it, that you weren't afraid. No wonder the ritual seemed to hold such power—here in the remote, inaccessible marshes of East Anglia, some remnant of man's ancient history had been preserved.

Tom swung the staff once, and tossed it on to the bonfire, where it landed in a shower of sparks. And then as the men lowered him to the ground, he held out his hands to Josey. At once she flew across and hurled herself into his arms, clinging to him in relief.

He laughed softly, stroking his hand down over her hair. 'Hey, hey—it's all right,' he soothed. 'There's no need to get so upset.'

'Why did you have to join in with that?' she demanded, her voice half-strangled. 'You could have got hurt.'

'Not really,' he insisted. 'It's not particularly dangerous, so long as you keep a steady hand and a cool head.'

'It *looked* dangerous.'

He laughed again, dismissing her fears. 'Come on, let's dance.'

The fiddler had struck up again, a lively jig, and Tom whirled her into the throng, spinning her round and round until she was dizzy and laughing, her head light. She hadn't forgotten that pagan scene—it seemed to replay in her head, over and over, halfway between dream and nightmare.

The bonfire was giving off lots of heat, crackling fiercely as it sent sparks and flames up into the dark sky. The fragrant sweetness of woodsmoke filled the air, a scent that Josey knew would always evoke memories of tonight, as long as she lived.

Tom had his arms tightly around her waist, and her arms were around his neck, curving her body close against his. She loved him so much that it hurt. If only he would tell her that he loved her too... But she could wait for that. Tonight, there would no longer be any reason to hold back. Tonight she could be his completely.

The effect of the strong ale was causing a certain amount of raucous merriment among some of the company, and Josey began to realise that they were being deliberately jostled as they danced. Some of the men were making muttered comments to Tom, winking broadly—it wasn't difficult to guess what they were saying.

'What's going on?' she demanded, a little annoyed.

Tom smiled, the light of the bonfire glinting in his eyes. 'Oh, it's just part of the old tradition,' he explained, a huskiness in his voice in spite of his efforts to sound as if he was joking. 'The prize for the winner of the Vanney Hal is supposed to be that he can spend the night with the maiden of his choice.'

'Oh...' She felt the hot colour run into her cheeks.

'Of course,' he demurred, the hint of a smile at the corner of his mouth inviting her to disagree with him, 'we won't be able to follow the tradition quite to the letter, will we? You're still married.'

'Well, as a matter of fact . . .' she lowered her lashes to veil her eyes '. . . I heard from my solicitor yesterday.'

'Yesterday?' For a brief second she was afraid that he was going to be angry with her for withholding the news from him, but then he drew her even closer in his arms, his breath warm against her cheek as he bent his head over hers. 'Well, in that case . . .'

Flames rose around them, hotter than the bonfire, consuming them as they clung together in a kiss so deep and passionate that it kindled their mutual hunger until it was almost uncontrollable. Josey had no thought of the other dancers all around them, watching them with indulgent amusement. She only knew that she wanted to make love with this man, to lie naked with him somewhere warm and quiet, to surrender her body totally to his.

She was barely aware that the music, and the heat of the bonfire, were fading. They were still dancing, slowly, lost in their own world. It was only after several moments that she became aware of the cool, quiet darkness, and the sweet smell of fresh hay.

She opened her eyes, and looked up to find herself beneath a high roof, laced with thick oak beams. 'Where are we?' she asked in a hushed whisper.

'Bill Whickham's barn.'

She knew it, slightly. It was at the bottom of the yard of Bill's substantial farmhouse, next to the foaling shed. Great bales of hay were piled six high, reaching almost to the roof—winter bedding and fodder for his valuable brood mares. There was a half-loft, piled with more hay, and a ladder stood against it. Tom urged her towards it, his eyes glinting with intent.

'Up you go,' he commanded softly.

'Up there?' Her voice shook with mingled apprehension and excitement as she twisted her head to look
up at the loft.

He nodded.

She hesitated a moment, struggling to frame into
words one thought that was still troubling her. 'Tom.
I... There's something that's been on my mind. It's
about Colin—sort of. And about us.'

He waited quietly for her to go on.

'It's just... I know there was Paula, of course, and
I know there must have been others. But I've no idea
who they were. And these days... well...'

He smiled down into her eyes as her voice trailed
away. 'I know what you're trying to say—I'd thought
about that, too. And the risk that you might get
pregnant.' He patted his back pocket. 'Don't worry—
I've taken care of it.'

'Oh...' She was caught between commending his
good sense, and a foolish disappointment that he
should have been so careful to avoid there being a
baby out of this. She looked up at him in accusing
indignation. 'You were very sure of me, weren't you?'

That low, husky laugh stroked over her senses. 'Oh,
yes—I was very sure. I don't think either of us were
strong enough to wait any longer. Now get up that
ladder,' he added, turning her round and nudging her
towards it, the brush of his body against hers warning
her of just how urgent was his hunger. 'Unless you
want me to take you right here on the floor.'

He dragged her down at once into the soft hay, and
they tumbled over each other, laughing, scrabbling
impatiently at each other's buttons, dragging at
clothes. The light of the bonfire, coming in through

the wide barn doors, flickered on the walls and roof, reflecting the fire in their blood.

But, at the same moment, they both seemed to realise that this was not a thing to be rushed. They stilled in their haste, lying back in the hay, gazing into each other's eyes. They had waited a long, long time for this, and neither of them wanted to do less than savour every last moment to the full.

Tom's breathing was husky and ragged as he slid his hand inside the loose front of her blouse, to stroke lightly over the aching swell of her breast, moulding it in his long, sensitive fingers. A small sigh escaped her lips as she closed her eyes, blissfully happy as he drew her into his arms.

Slowly, almost reverently, he unfastened the remaining buttons, and drew the fabric aside. Many times in the past few weeks he had undressed her like this, but this time they both knew it was different. This time there would be no stopping, no holding back—this time they were going all the way.

Teasingly, he let his finger trace the lacy pattern of her bra. It was so fine and delicate that the dark shadow of her nipple showed through, a taut nub crushed against the fabric. Slowly he circled it, tantalising, making her groan in an agony of expectation.

His kisses dusted lightly over her face, brushing her trembling eyelids, finding the tiny pulse that fluttered beneath her temple. The musky, masculine scent of his skin was filling her senses, drugging her, and she was torn between a longing for him to do more and a desire to linger for ever in the rapture of each moment.

'I want you so much, Josey,' he breathed against her ear as he deftly unfastened the clip of her bra. 'I want to caress every inch of you. Your skin's like silk...' His hand slid smoothly over her rounded, naked breast, cupping it with a gentle possessiveness, his thumb brushing over the hardened, tender nipple.

A shimmer of heat ran through her. He had taken the taut bud between his fingers, plucking at it and rolling it, shafting sparks of pleasure through her. And as her head tipped back into the crook of his arm his hot mouth began to trail down the long, vulnerable curve of her throat, scalding it with kisses.

She wanted him to kiss her breasts, and she curved her spine, offering herself invitingly. He laughed softly, low in his throat, taking his time. 'You have the most beautiful body,' he murmured. 'Your breasts are perfect—firm, and ripe, and just big enough to fit into my hand. And they taste...' he bent his head to lap at one tautly expectant bud with his rasping tongue '...like honey.'

His tongue swirled around the pink, tender nipple in languorous sensuality, as if he was tasting the sweet cherry atop an ice-cream sundae. She sighed deeply, stretching her arms above her head in feline pleasure, delighting in being his icon and his slave. His strong, hard teeth were inflicting tiny bites, not sharp enough for real pain, and she challenged him with a laugh, defying his power.

With a low growl he slid his arms beneath her, lifting her in a helpless arc, and his mouth descended on her tender, aching breast, taking the exquisitely sensitised nipple and suckling it deeply, hungrily. He paused only to subject the other to the same sweet punishment, and she moaned as the pleasure pulsed through her in hot waves, her fingers tangling in the crisp curls at the nape of his neck as she held him fiercely to her.

The fire caught at them both again, and in a fevered impatience for the feel of naked skin against naked skin they stripped off their own clothes, until she was wearing nothing but a pair of tiny lace briefs, and he only his jeans. Then he drew her back into his arms again, taking one of her hands in his; but suddenly she knew what he wanted her to do, and all her nervous apprehension came flooding back.

'Don't be afraid,' he murmured, gentle but insistent. 'There's nothing to be frightened of.'

Cradling her in his arms, and murmuring to her in soft reassurance, he guided her hand down to stroke against him, through the thick fabric of his jeans. A tremor ran through her as she became aware of the sheer masculine power in him, but the fear was subsiding. She knew that she could trust him implicitly, that he would give her nothing but the most exquisite pleasure.

And, in return, she wanted to give him pleasure. As her confidence slowly returned, her boldness grew, and she began to caress him willingly. He lay back against a bale of hay, his hands behind his head, his eyes smiling encouragement.

Daring, she knelt over him, straddling across his lap, and laying both hands along his cheeks she brushed her lips lightly over his temples, his eyelids, his mouth. He was letting her take control—only a man who had nothing at all to prove could be so totally relaxed.

Her temperature was rising, her blood pounding in her veins, making her forget everything but the aching hunger that was rising inside her. She closed her eyes, all her mind focused on measuring his responses as she probed with her tongue into the small hollow behind his ear, finding to her delight that he was as sensitive there as she was herself.

It was delicious, this unfamiliar sensation of her own power. Her hands smoothed over his warm male skin, thrilling to the solid bulk of muscle in his shoulders; she trailed her fingers playfully through the rough smattering of dark hair across his wide chest, teasing the flat male nipples with her circling tongue until he growled a warning.

Then she moved on, her heart beating faster as she traversed the hard, ridged plane of his stomach, until she reached the barrier of his jeans. There she paused, contemplating the thick leather belt, not sure if she had the courage to go further.

He waited, not pressuring her, his hand reaching up to stroke her hair in gentle reassurance. But there was a compulsion driving her, too powerful to evade. Her small hands struggled with the heavy silver buckle, and he laughed softly as he came to her assistance. And then, her mouth dry, she drew down the thick zip of his jeans.

All the instincts of Eve had awoken inside her, teaching her things she would never have dreamed of in her wildest fantasies. Her careful hands, and her warm, eager mouth, caressed him in devoted homage, finding the most inventive ways to arouse him, her heart fluttering as the powerful tremors of male arousal running through him warned her of just how much he was going to demand of her.

Her whole body was burning with an un-quenchable fever, and her head felt light as she rose to her feet. The lacy scrap of her briefs was really no covering at all, but she hesitated, a little shy again; and then very slowly she eased the tiny lace briefs down over her slim thighs, and tossed them aside with her other clothes.

And then she stood there, letting him look at her, trembling slightly, her soft naked skin blushed with the glow of the distant bonfire, watching his face through the veil of her lashes as his gaze lingered over every slender curve.

There was no mistaking his satisfaction. 'Beautiful,' he murmured, his eyes kindling with desire. 'And all mine.'

'Yes,' she whispered; she wanted to add that she was his forever, but that seemed a little presumptuous, when he hadn't said that that was what he wanted.

He held out his hand to her. 'Come here,' he commanded softly.

She went to him, and he caught both her hands, pulling her down to kneel across his lap again. Her cheeks flamed scarlet as he held out a small foil pack to her. 'I . . . I'm not really sure how to use these,' she stammered.

'Just do what comes naturally,' he murmured, smiling.

'I've always thought . . . I was afraid they would spoil the pleasure.'

He laughed softly, shaking his head. 'Nothing is going to spoil the pleasure of this,' he assured her, his eyes caressing every slender curve of her body.

She lowered her silken lashes to shadow her cheeks, her breath held in her throat as she fumbled with the tiny packet.

'Use your teeth,' he suggested.

She looked into his eyes, suddenly bold, flashing her strong white teeth as she slit the foil open. And

then with the gentlest care she began to caress him
again, as she smoothed the gossamer-fine sheath into
place.

'You see?' He caught her arms, laughing as he drew
her up against him. 'It was easy, wasn't it?'

His hands were stroking over her slender thighs,
and his rough jaw rasped against her soft skin as he
buried his face in the warm valley between her breasts.
She let go her breath in a long, shuddering sigh, her
head tipped dizzily back as he dusted them with
scorching kisses, lapping and nibbling and suckling
at the tender, ripe berries of her nipples until she was
writhing in an agony of sensual pleasure, her spine
curving in ecstasy.

She was totally vulnerable to him, her thighs spread
apart across the width of his body, and as he laid her
back slowly in the warm hay, leaning over her, the
powerful muscles in his shoulders hunched as he held
his weight from crushing her, she felt a quiver of pure
feminine submissiveness run through her.

She could only yield to the sweetly intimate touch
of his fingers, gently seeking amid the secret folds of
velvet. And then she caught her breath on a sharp sob
of pleasure as he found his treasure, the tiny seed-
pearl that was the focus of all her sensitivity.

The pagan fire of those ancient demons was burning
inside her, consuming her. His head had bent again
over her breasts, feasting on them as if they were ripe
fruits; and then his kisses moved on, lower, over the
peach-smooth curve of her stomach, and down to the
soft cluster of curls that crowned the parting of her
thighs. Her breath seemed to stop in her throat. This
was so intimate, so exquisite—the hot tip of his tongue
had slipped in to take over the task of arousing her

responses, until she was melting like warm honey, lost in the sheer sensuality of his caress.

The hay was as soft and cosy as the finest feather bed, cradling her as if in a dream. The only light was the flickering orange glow of the distant bonfire, and she could still hear the fiddler playing, his music sweet on the night air.

He took her with one deep, hard thrust, that almost took her breath away. Pausing, he smiled down into her eyes. 'All right?' he asked in soft concern.

'Oh, yes...' She moved beneath him, her eyes provocatively inviting.

He stroked her hair back from her face in a gesture of the utmost tenderness. 'Oh, Josey—you're so beautiful,' he murmured as he began to move inside her with a slow, powerful rhythm. 'I've wanted you so much.'

Sweet tears were spilling over her cheeks as she felt the joy of being one with him; it was the most beautiful experience of her life. She ran her hands up over his sweat-slicked body, holding her to him; he was so strong, so uncompromisingly masculine, and she felt so delicate, so exquisitely feminine as she lay beneath him.

He wasn't gentle—his own need was too strong. But she didn't care. Her body submitted willingly to every powerful thrust, surrendering all he demanded and more. As they moved together in this erotic, primeval dance she felt the mounting surge of her own response, sweeping her up to the dizziest heights, and their breathing was harsh and ragged as they soared together like raging flames, swirling in an incandescent heat that was exploding around them in a conflagration that was consuming them, leaving them to fall at last, sated and exhausted, tangled up in each other's arms.

CHAPTER TEN

'COME September you'll be bored stiff, and dying to get back to London.'

Well, it was several weeks into September, and Josey had no plans to return to London at all. Lying back against the pillows of the big bed she had bought for her cottage—Aunt Floss's would have been much too small, even if it had still been in reasonable condition—Josey sighed contentedly.

Beside her, Tom propped his head up on his elbow, and smiled down into her eyes. 'You look like the cat that's got the cream,' he teased.

'Mmm.' She snuggled up against him. 'The very *best* cream.'

He laughed—that low, husky, seductive laugh that always made her spine shiver—and let one idle fingertip trail lingeringly down over the curves of her body. 'Do you know, you've got just about the sexiest——?' The insistent bleep of his telephone pager interrupted him. 'Blast! I wish I'd turned that damned thing off.'

Josey felt that familiar sense of deflation as he reached across her to pick up the telephone. Another sick horse, or a cow having a difficult labour, summoning him away from her side. She couldn't mind, of course—she had known when this thing started what it was going to be like.

'OK, I'll be right there.' Tom put down the phone, and bent his head to kiss her, long and lingeringly.

But she was familiar enough with his goodbye kisses by now to know that he wasn't going to be staying. It was only a moment before he rolled off the bed, and began to pull on his clothes.

Maybe it wouldn't be quite so bad, she reflected, if he would only stay all night when he could. But he never did, even though it was often two o'clock in the morning before he left. And he never told her when he was going to see her again, either. In effect, it had been every evening so far, but she still never felt quite sure.

Pulling on his jacket, he came over to stand beside the bed, grinning down at her as she lay there on top of the covers, still naked as she had been when he had carried her in here from the kitchen, when the overwhelming urge to make love had caught up with them—in the middle of clearing away the romantic dinner she had cooked for him earlier in the evening.

'You look like a dream,' he chuckled, a spark of fire in his eyes.

She stretched sensuously, like a cat, her smile inviting. 'Well, you could always come back later and finish dreaming me,' she suggested hopefully.

The spark flickered out. 'Not tonight,' he said, shaking his head. 'I'd better be going.' He leaned over and dropped a light kiss on the tip of her nose, and then briskly left the room. Laying back, she closed her eyes, listening as he let himself out of the front door, started up the Land Rover, and drove away.

One small tear escaped from the corner of her eye, and trickled down her cheek. Without him, the bed seemed so big and cold. Why wouldn't he stay, even for just one night? She was almost ready to beg.

*   *   *

But by the morning she was able to don the façade of composure that enabled her to continue some semblance of normal life. She knew quite well that Tom would dislike any appearance of clinginess on her part, so she always did her best to appear cool and content.

Sandra was in the clinic when she arrived, and greeted her with cheerful friendliness. All that old hostility was gone—since the night of Vanney Hal, according to Vi, young Frank Whickham had been hanging around rather a lot.

'Has Tom gone out?' she enquired, picking up the post from the reception counter.

'I don't think he's been in, actually,' Sandra responded. 'I think he's still down at Bill Whickham's stables—he's got a mare in foal, and they've been expecting trouble.'

'Oh . . .' Josey felt a twinge of guilt for wishing he'd stayed with her last night. He had a job to do, one that was very important—if he was called out, he had to go. 'I'll see if Vi's got the kettle on,' she suggested. 'Fancy a cup of tea?'

'Yes, please... Ah, here's Tom now—he must have heard you mention the kettle!' added Sandra with a laugh.

The Land Rover had indeed just pulled in to its parking-space beside the surgery. Tom looked weary as he climbed out. Josey watched him with a sinking heart—she knew before he even opened the door that for once he had lost the battle. She hurried over to meet him, wanting only to do what she could to soothe him.

'Tom . . .?'

His eyes were hard, and barely flickered towards her. 'Good morning,' he rapped, as if she were no more to him than just a rather irritating nuisance, and without another word he marched straight across the room and into the office, letting the door close behind him.

Josey stared after him in shock, but Sandra responded with the wry smile of one who had seen it all before. 'He's upset,' she explained. 'He doesn't mean to be rude.'

'No,' agreed Josey—she had already guessed as much for herself, though it didn't really help. 'I'll make him some coffee.'

She hurried through to the kitchen, where Vi already had the kettle on. Her hand was shaking slightly as she made the coffee—just the way he liked it—and carried it carefully back to the office. She tapped nervously on the door, but there was no response, so she opened it anyway.

Tom was sitting with his elbows propped up on the desk, his head in his hands. Josey ached to just reach out and touch him, bring him some kind of comfort, but every inch of him seemed to bristle with rejection. 'Tom?' she began diffidently. 'I've...brought you some coffee.'

He sat up, holding out a peremptory hand for the cup. 'Thank you.'

She hesitated, lost for anything else to say in the face of such an impenetrable barrier. As she hovered, uncertain, he gave her a hard, enquiring look, as if he was expecting her to speak or leave the room. 'I...I've done the Ministry returns,' she stammered. 'They're all ready for you to sign.'

'All right,' he snapped. 'Later.'

Still she hovered in the doorway, hating to feel so rejected. 'I'm so sorry, Tom,' she managed, her voice unsteady. 'Did you . . . did you manage to save either of them?'

'No,' he responded shortly. 'The foal was deformed and I had to do an emergency Caesarean. If I'd known about it sooner . . .'

'But you couldn't have,' she insisted, knowing that if it had been possible he would surely have known.

'Oh, I could have,' he countered bitterly. 'If I could afford to buy a scanner . . . But you're talking a hell of a lot of money.'

Josey blinked at him in surprise. If it was just a question of money—she could easily sell a few of her shares . . . 'I could buy it for you,' she offered eagerly. 'How much would you need, exactly——?'

'*No!*'

She had begun to move towards him, but the cold anger in his eyes stopped her in her tracks. 'I could afford it,' she argued. 'If you wanted to, you could pay me back . . .'

'Oh, yes. I know you can afford it,' he sneered, his voice lashing her with cynical contempt. 'You've got money to burn now, haven't you? Well, thank you, but I don't want your charity.'

'It's not charity!' she retorted hotly. 'I *want* to buy it for you. What's the use of having all that money if I can't do something useful with it? I want to help you, that's all.' She moved towards him again, longing to have him take her in his arms, but that cold, shuttered look was back in his eyes again, that look that she hadn't seen for weeks.

'I don't need your help,' he snarled. 'Keep your money. Buy yourself another Porsche.'

'I don't want another Porsche,' she protested, her voice wavering. 'I want you. But you never even let me get close.'

He lifted one dark eyebrow in cruel mockery. 'Don't I?' He let his gaze drift down over her body in a sardonic appraisal. 'It seems to me we've been just about as close as two people can get.'

She stared at him, acid tears pricking the backs of her eyes. 'Is that all it is to you?' she queried bleakly. 'Just sex?'

'What are you complaining about?' he threw back at her harshly. 'I helped you sort out your hang-ups about it. Now you can go back to London and——'

'You helped me sort out my hang-ups?' she repeated, startled. 'Oh, it was some sort of therapy, was it? Well, thank you for the treatment, Doctor. I feel absolutely wonderful now.'

'Look.' He was beginning to get really angry. 'I never made you any promises. If you want some nice cosy little domestic scene, you'd better find yourself someone else. I thought I'd made that clear from the beginning. That's the way it is—take it or leave it.'

Josey felt her heart freezing over. 'I see,' she responded, struggling for as much dignity as she could muster. 'In that case, I think I'll leave it. I spent nine years in one bad relationship—I don't need another. Please don't come to my cottage again—I don't want to see you. And I think it would be a good idea if you found someone else to do your office work, too.'

Josey retreated, stunned by the suddenness of the quarrel. All her heart prompted her to go back in there and say she was sorry, beg him to make up—but something held her back. That was what she had always done with Colin and she had ended up as a doormat. She wasn't going to make that mistake again.

It was no excuse that he was tired and upset. Maybe she had been wrong to offer to buy the scanner—it had probably wounded his pride. But she had done it in good faith, out of a spirit of generosity—there had been no need for him to bite her head off like that.

And after all, it wasn't as if things had been exactly perfect between them, she acknowledged wryly. She had been right—he wouldn't let her get close. Sometimes, in the intimate after-glow of their love-making, she could almost let herself imagine that he cared for her more deeply than he was willing to admit, but that feeling would soon fade as he got out of bed and put his clothes on, leaving her without any compunction.

No, she was doing the right thing, she told herself firmly, brushing away the tears. If he wanted her back, he would know where to find her. But he would have to apologise—and in future, he would have to treat her a great deal better.

'Oh, what a lovely tree!' Helen exclaimed, gazing in admiration at the large Christmas tree Josey had just finished decorating. 'You've really made this place cosy.'

Josey smiled. 'It's so nice to have a place all of my own, that I can have exactly as I want it. We never used to have a Christmas tree in London—Colin thought they were too kitsch. No, Pepper, you can't play with that, love,' she added, quickly snatching up the silver ball that had fallen from the Christmas tree before the little dog could attack it and maybe hurt herself.

'So listen, what are you doing for Christmas dinner tomorrow?' asked Helen. 'Are you going to come over to us?'

Josey shook her head wistfully. 'I don't think so,' she demurred. 'It's lovely of you to ask me, Helen, but not if Tom's going to be there. It would just make for an awkward atmosphere, and spoil things for everyone. I've never been so embarrassed as the last time, when he just walked out like that, without even a word to his mother.'

Helen had the grace to look guilty. 'I know. I'm sorry about that, Josey. I really shouldn't have asked you both, without telling either of you the other was going to be there. I just wanted to get the two of you back together again.'

Josey shook her head. 'That's up to him,' she insisted.

Helen sighed. 'You two—you're the most obstinate pair I ever met. What on earth went wrong between you? It seemed to be going so well.'

'I don't want to talk about it,' Josey insisted, evading her friend's eyes. 'It just didn't work out.'

'But you still care about him, don't you? How can you let it carry on like this? He's so unhappy—I know he is. Since you split up, he's had a temper on him like a stuck bull. Sandra's handed in her notice, and even Vi's thinking of chucking it in.'

Josey shrugged. 'He always was bad-tempered— that's nothing to do with me.'

'I've never known him like this,' Helen asserted. 'He doesn't seem to care about anything—Sandra says he doesn't open his post for weeks at a time. His accounts are all in a mess, and the Ministry's on his back for his returns. He'll ruin his practice, and go bankrupt, if he doesn't sort himself out soon.'

'Oh, I dare say he could do with a *secretary*,' Josey conceded with a touch of asperity. 'In fact, what he really needs is a robot, to do everything for him, and not mind being yelled at like an idiot for the slightest mistake. I don't blame Sandra for giving in her notice—he's lucky she didn't do it years ago.'

Helen shook her head. 'What he needs is you. Over the summer, when the two of you were together, he was like a different person. Won't you even just *try*?'

Josey faced her friend, resolutely resisting her persuasion. 'When *he* says he needs me, maybe I will. But don't hold your breath, Helen. He doesn't want to admit he needs anybody.'

But, in spite of her determination, Josey felt a sadness descending over her as evening drew in. She could just imagine the lively scene in the farmhouse on Christmas Day, with the children rushing to open their presents, and everyone sitting down together to Christmas dinner. She would have loved to have been there—she would have loved to have been with Tom.

Pepper seemed to sense her mood, and scrambled up on to her lap, nuzzling against her as if to comfort her. She stroked the warm little body affectionately. 'I know,' she murmured. 'You loved him, too, didn't you? But it was no good—he just didn't love me. It's better this way. And we've still got each other.'

The little puppy barked agreement, and jumped down off her lap to scamper off round the room, looking for something to play with.

Josey leaned back in her armchair, and closed her eyes, thinking over what Helen had said. If only she could be as sure that the reason for his temper, his lack of interest in his paperwork, was because he was missing her. But she was very much afraid that Helen was just being romantic.

One subject that they hadn't talked about, that they had both seemed to avoid, was the rumour circulating in the village that Vanessa was pregnant. Of course, she didn't *really* believe, not for one moment, that Tom had anything to do with it—not really. She would just have liked to have known what Helen thought.

Even so—— 'Pepper! Oh my God, what have you done?' The pup had been happily playing with something on the floor, and suddenly she had let out a squeak of alarm. And, to Josey's absolute horror, she saw a pool of blood spilling around her paw.

That silver ball—it had fallen down from the Christmas tree again, and shattered into sharp little shards of glass. In a surge of desperate panic, Josey scooped her up, and ran into the kitchen to snatch a towel to wrap her in, and then raced out to the car.

It was a nightmare drive to the village, at top speed. Poor little Pepper was bleeding so badly—there was blood everywhere. 'Oh, please, don't die,' she whispered, tears standing in her eyes. 'Please, Pepper, hold on—we'll be there in a minute.'

She swerved the car into the kerb outside the surgery, and slammed on the brakes. What she would have done if Tom had been out on a call she didn't know, but to her blessed relief there was a light on in the kitchen, and as she scrambled out of the car the front door opened.

'Josey!' Tom was halfway down the path. 'Whatever's the matter?'

'It's Pepper.' She put the precious bundle straight into his arms. 'She's cut her paw, and she's bleeding really badly.'

'Come inside.'

He hurried straight through to the surgery, and put Pepper down on the examination table, unwrapping her carefully from the folds of blood-stained towel. Immediately she jumped up, trying to lick his face and getting blood all over his shirt.

He laughed. 'Well, for a puppy that's supposed to be bleeding to death, you look remarkably lively,' he scolded her playfully. 'Come on, let me have a look at this paw, then.'

Josey held the wriggling little body still as he examined the injury. Pepper *did* seem remarkably untroubled by the cut—after that first surprised squawk, she hadn't whined at all. 'She *has* cut herself,' she insisted, 'Look at all that blood on the towel.'

Tom nodded. 'Oh, she's cut herself, all right. But it looks a great deal worse than it really is. It's always like that when they cut a pad—it looks like pints of blood. But she'll be all right—the bleeding's almost stopped already.'

Josey was feeling dizzy with relief. 'Will you need to put stitches in it?' she asked anxiously.

He shook his head. 'Best not to—she's cut a kind of flap of skin, and you have to be quite careful. I'll put a dressing on it, and give her some antibiotics. Try to make her keep the dressing on as long as possible—though I don't suppose that'll be very easy,' he added with a dry laugh.

'No, it won't,' she agreed wryly. 'Thank you, Tom. I...I thought she was going to die.' Suddenly the tears welled up, and at once he came round and took her into his arms, his hand stroking down over her hair. That just made her cry all the more—she had missed him so much, missed the feel of his strong arms around her. She never wanted to let him go again.

'It's all right, Josey,' he murmured softly, kissing away the tears. 'Everything's going to be all right.'

'Oh, Tom . . .' She lifted her face, and their mouths melted together in a kiss that held all the tenderness of three long months of heartbreak.

'Come back to me, Josey,' he begged, holding her close. 'I've been so stupid and stubborn, refusing to admit to myself that I love you. But I've wanted you so much—I *need* you. It doesn't matter if you decide later that you want to move back to London—I'll come with you. I can get a practice there. I can live anywhere, so long as it's with you.'

She gazed up into his eyes, her heart spilling over. 'Oh, no,' she whispered. I don't want to go back to London. I love it here—I don't ever want to move away.'

'Are you sure?' His eyes searched hers anxiously. 'You're not just saying that?'

She shook her head. 'I'm not Julia, Tom,' she reminded him, determined to bury the past once and for all.

He smiled wryly. 'No, you're not. And I should have known that. You're so very different from her. You accused me once that it was just sex between us, but it was with Julia that it was like that. Hell, we were far too young, we had nothing in common. I let myself be dazzled by how gorgeous she was, and then I woke up one morning about three months after I'd married her and realised that I didn't even particularly like her.'

'And yet you stayed with her?'

'Of course. I kept trying—I *had* married her, after all. And I suppose I was too proud to admit I'd made a mistake, as well. Maybe it would have been better if we'd both cut our losses right away—at least we'd have saved ourselves four years of misery. And after it was over I vowed I would never make that mistake again. Until you shunted your way into my life,' he added with a soft laugh. 'I took one look at you in the wreck of that car, and I knew you were going to turn me inside out.'

She nestled against him contentedly. 'A bird with a broken wing,' she murmured. 'You never could resist rescuing them, could you?'

'But when they were healed, I always had to let them fly away. And I thought I would have to do the same with you. That was why I was always afraid to let you get too close. I was afraid to let myself need you too much. I wouldn't even let myself stay all night with you—I could have got too used to it, waking up in the mornings and finding you there beside me. And then if you'd left me, it would have been like tearing my heart out.'

She put her hands along each side of his face, feeling the rasp of his hard jaw beneath her fingertips. 'I'm not going to leave you,' she asserted. 'You're stuck with me for life. I won't be expecting any nice cosy domestic scenes . . .'

'You'd better,' he contradicted her. 'Because that's what I want. When I've been out on an emergency late at night, and it's all cold and miserable outside, I want to come home and find you there with a kiss to warm me up. I want to look up from the paper on a Sunday afternoon and find you sitting on the other side of the fireplace, or go into my office and find you've put a damned silly bowl of roses on my desk.'

'Ah, so that's it!' she teased, laughing up at him. 'Helen told me how you've been neglecting your paperwork. No wonder you want me back—you need a secretary again!'

'I don't want a secretary,' he growled impatiently, crushing her against him. 'I want you.'

She wrapped her arms around him, breathing with bliss the subtle musky maleness of his body. 'And are you going to let me buy you that scanner?' she enquired, pressing home her point while she felt confident of having the advantage.

'You can buy me whatever you want—I'll make you a list, if you like. What's money? I used to get angry when Julia criticised me for not having enough—it would be just plain stupid to let the fact that you've got too much come between us.'

Josey laughed happily, wrapping her arms around his neck. 'That's what I've always thought,' she declared. 'Anyway, I've got far more than I need, even though I've given a lot of it to charities and things. And even if——'

But Pepper, at that moment, decided that the interest had been diverted from her for long enough, and began to protest—after all, she was supposed to be the patient. Tom laughed, and let Josey go. 'All right—let's see about a dressing for this silly dog's paw, then,' he conceded.

'Oh, she's not so silly,' Josey argued, laughing happily. 'She got us back together again, which is more than Helen could do.'

'You'll come over to Christmas dinner tomorrow?' he asked. 'Helen would never forgive me if I don't take you.'

'Of course.'

She held Pepper for him as he dressed her paw, wrapping a bandage tightly all the way up her leg. Then he gave her a shot of antibiotic, and something to quieten her down for a while so that hopefully she wouldn't pull the bandage off quite so quickly, and would give the cut a chance to heal properly.

The little pup was sleepy almost at once, and Josey picked her up, giving her a hug. Tom put his arm around her as they walked through to the kitchen. As they passed the office, she glanced in, smiling wryly at the mess. 'It looks as though you do need me,' she remarked drily. 'Haven't you filed *anything* since I left?'

'No,' he admitted, dropping a light kiss on the end of her nose. 'I'm completely helpless without you. Come back and sort me out.'

The Norfolk landscape was bleak in the grip of December—dark and damp, and drifted with cold shreds of mist that lay low across the fields. In the midst of it, the Quinn farmhouse looked like a haven of life and warmth. Fairy-lights twinkled from a small Christmas tree set up in the porch, and a wisp of smoke rose from the chimney, promising a roaring fire inside.

Josey glanced at Tom as he drove the Land Rover down the long, Roman-straight road between the flat fields, and smiled. He smiled back, that wonderful smile that she had missed so much these past three months. She felt so happy—there was just one tiny question niggling at the back of her mind.

'Have you heard about Vanessa?' she enquired innocently.

He lifted one enquiring eyebrow. 'You mean about the baby? Yes, Gerry told me. He's over the moon.'

'Is he?'

He must have caught the slight note of constraint in her voice, and slanted her a questioning glance. 'He's wanted to start a family for a long time—I think he'd almost given up trying to persuade her. But all of a sudden she changed her mind—and now apparently she's as chuffed about it as he is.'

'That's good.' She was aware of a small surge of relief—though of course there had never been any *real* doubt. 'I liked Gerry.'

'Yes, he's a good bloke. I'm glad he and Vanessa seem to be getting along better at last.'

'Instead of her trying to make eyes at you?' she suggested teasingly.

He laughed wryly. 'Yes, if you like,' he conceded. 'It was always a bit awkward, that.'

'She's very beautiful,' Josey remarked, at last having the courage to probe his thoughts a little.

'Yes, she is,' he agreed, so readily that she knew he was hiding nothing. 'But she was always just the girl next door, to me. I know everyone had us down as an item when we were younger, but I never saw it that way. I suppose it was hard on Vanessa—it took her a long time to really understand how I felt.'

Josey smiled, and leaned her head against his shoulder. 'Ah, well, she's happy now,' she concluded with a glow of satisfaction. 'They both are.'

'Yes.' He paused at the gate, as the children, who had been watching from the window, raced out to open it. 'And maybe,' he suggested, rubbing his cheek against her hair, 'if that little madam in the back seat won't get too jealous, we could think about doing something like it ourselves in the not too distant future.'

'You mean have a baby?' she queried breathlessly.

'Of course. Why not?'

'Oh . . . yes!'

There was no further chance to talk. The children had yanked open the door, all chattering excitedly, and Pepper was barking to jump down and play with them. 'Careful with her, you lot,' warned Tom firmly. 'She's hurt her paw, and she's not to pull that bandage off. Just carry her into the kitchen, and get her to lie down.'

He swung out of the car, and came round to take Josey's hand. Helen was in the doorway, her face wreathed in smiles, and Tom's mother was close behind her, looking just as delighted.

'You came!' cried Helen, darting forward to hug her. 'You made it up after all.' She grinned up at her brother-in-law in triumph.

'Yes—thanks to Pepper cutting her foot last night,' he told her. 'Now, where's . . .? Ah, good, you've put it up in the same place as usual. Come here, Josey.'

She blinked in surprise as he drew her into the house, and positioned her very precisely just inside the doorway. Looking up, she found that she was standing exactly under a large sprig of mistletoe.

'There.' He took her into his arms, and kissed her long and deeply—in fact so long that she began to wonder if he had forgotten that his whole family were standing there watching them.

'Tom...!' she protested, trying to draw back a little.

He lifted his head, and gazed down into her eyes. 'I love you, Josey,' he murmured.

'Oh, and I love you too,' she returned, hugging him.

He kept his arm around her, and turned to face the interested audience.

'I've got something to tell you,' he announced proudly.

'*We've* got something to tell you,' she corrected him, laughingly insistent.

He nodded. 'Josey and I have got something to tell you. We're getting married.'

There was an explosion of delight all around them. Josey found herself hugged and kissed by everyone—even the reserved Donald—as Tom accepted their warm congratulations.

'When's the wedding?' demanded Helen.

'Can I be bridesmaid?' pleaded little Sara, clinging to Josey's legs and gazing up at her imploringly.

'Of course you can, darling,' Josey promised. 'We haven't actually decided on the date yet——'

Suddenly Tom's pager began to bleep insistently. 'Oh...' He swallowed his usual curse, in consideration of the children's listening ears. 'Put my dinner in the oven?' he asked his mother in wry resignation.

Josey smiled up at him, and lifted her arms to wrap them around his neck. 'Never mind,' she whispered softly, close to his ear. 'I'll still be here when you get back.'

Next Month's Romances

Each month you can choose from a world of variety in romance with Mills & Boon. Below are the new titles to look out for next month, why not ask either Mills & Boon Reader Service or your Newsagent to reserve you a copy of the titles you want to buy — just tick the titles you would like to order and either post to Reader Service or take it to any Newsagent and ask them to order your books.

Please save me the following titles:		Please tick	√
A HONEYED SEDUCTION	**Diana Hamilton**		
PASSIONATE POSSESSION	**Penny Jordan**		
MOTHER OF THE BRIDE	**Carole Mortimer**		
DARK ILLUSION	**Patricia Wilson**		
FATE OF HAPPINESS	**Emma Richmond**		
THE ALPHA MAN	**Kay Thorpe**		
HUNGARIAN RHAPSODY	**Jessica Steele**		
(This book is free with THE ALPHA MAN)			
NOTHING LESS THAN LOVE	**Vanessa Grant**		
LOVE'S VENDETTA	**Stephanie Howard**		
CALL UP THE WIND	**Anne McAllister**		
TOUCH OF FIRE	**Joanna Neil**		
TOMORROW'S HARVEST	**Alison York**		
THE STOLEN HEART	**Amanda Browning**		
NO MISTAKING LOVE	**Jessica Hart**		
THE BEGINNING OF THE AFFAIR	**Marjorie Lewty**		
CAUSE FOR LOVE	**Kerry Allyne**		
RAPTURE IN THE SANDS	**Sandra Marton**		

If you would like to order these books from Mills & Boon Reader Service please send £1.70 per title to: Mills & Boon Reader Service, P.O. Box 236, Croydon, Surrey, CR9 3RU and quote your Subscriber No:...(If applicable) and complete the name and address details below. Alternatively, these books are available from many local Newsagents including W.H.Smith, J.Menzies, Martins and other paperback stockists from 11th September 1992.

Name:...

Address:..

....Post Code:......................

To Retailer: If you would like to stock M&B books please contact your regular book/magazine wholesaler for details.

You may be mailed with offers from other reputable companies as a result of this application. If you would rather not take advantage of these opportunities please tick box ☐